Grammar

8

TEACHERS AT WORK

Sadlier School

Grammar

Teachers at work™ an imprint of Sadlier School, was created by teachers with teachers in mind to provide the right materials to support students with achieving academic success. Teachers all over the country contributed their ideas and expertise to bring together opportunities for students to practice essential skills and strategies with engaging print and online resources. Together they built a program that will support both teachers and students. We are excited to share these engaging print and online resources with you.

Sadlier School

Cover Series Design: Studio Montage, St. Louis, MO, United States of America

For additional online resources, go to sadlierconnect.com.

 is a trademark of William H. Sadlier, Inc.

William H. Sadlier, Inc.
9 Pine Street
New York, NY 10005-4700

Printed in the U.S.A.
ISBN: 978-1-4217-4708-8
1 2 3 4 5 6 7 8 9   19 18 17 16 15

PREFACE

Teachers at work™ is excited to introduce this new series to support students in mastering the Common Core State Standards.

The *Let's Target* series was developed by teachers. We understand students need to be engaged in their learning to succeed. With a simple, yet systematic approach, students learn skills and gain confidence to successfully meet the Common Core Standards.

"I got it!" That's what we want students to say when they focus on the lessons in the *Let's Target* series. As teachers, we know how hard it can be to find the right material to boost student achievement. With the *Let's Target* series, students complete the exercises in the book and then go online to reinforce what they have learned.

Want to flip it? Go ahead! Begin with the online resources to jumpstart the learning and then complement the activities with lessons from the book. Either way, students and teachers will be happy to get more opportunities to learn and practice essential skills.

Do you want to work independently or with a peer? *Let's Target* allows for all different kinds of learning strategies. Teachers will find more guidance about this in their Teacher's Guides.

Getting ready for Common Core Assessments? Since the beginning of the Common Core State Standards many have wondered how to prepare students for success. With *Let's Target Grammar*, students will strengthen grammar, usage, and mechanics, and build proficiency in the conventions of standard English.

Let's Target Grammar **for summer learning?** Students will review major concepts to hone grammar understanding and usage and come back to school ready for success!

Hey Students! Demonstrate your independence in understanding the conventions of standard English with the opportunities set forth in this book. Give yourself a push to be successful on the new Common Core assessments by mastering these grammar skills.

The components of the *Let's Target* series include:
- Student Editions with lots of opportunities for **"I got it!"** moments
- Teacher's Guides which support teachers with **CCSS connections** and problem solutions
- Online Resources give students and teachers the tools to **blend learning** and engage in learning in the classroom and at home

Teachers from around the country collaborated through Teachers at work ™, contributing ideas and expertise, to develop this series to prepare students for academic success. Please let us know if you have any ideas that will support students in reaching school success! Contact us at TeachersAtWork@Sadlier.com

Teachers at work

CONTENTS

CONTENTS

CONTENTS

CONTENTS

CONTENTS

CONTENTS

REDUCTION: ADJECTIVE CLAUSES TO PHRASES

PHRASAL VERBS

APPENDIX

POINTS /12

EXERCISE **1**   *VERBALS*

- Verbals are words formed from verbs but function as a different part of speech.
- Verbals can be gerunds. A gerund is a verbal that ends in "-ing." It acts as a noun. [Example: She enjoys <u>dancing</u>. <u>Reading</u> is a good habit to have.]
- Verbals can also be used as participles. A participle is a verbal that often ends in "-ing" or "-ed." It acts as an adjective. It tells more about the noun that follows it. [Example: The <u>interesting</u> movie broke the box office records over the weekend. My hands <u>trembling</u>, I approached the bully.]
- Verbals can also be used as infinitives. An infinitive is a verbal that consists of "to" and a verb. An infinitive acts as a noun, an adjective or an adverb. It shows the purpose of the action. [Example: She decided <u>to learn</u> Spanish.]

Fill in the blanks with the correct form of the verbals in the parentheses. State whether the verbal is a gerund (G), a participle (P) or an infinitive (I).

1   The _____ girl returned to her room after her parents told her that the trip to New York had been canceled. (disappoint)

                   _____

2   _____ a movie is my favorite pastime. (watch)   _____

3   When did you learn _____? (cycle)   _____

4   The _____ sun cast an orange hue over the countryside. (rise)   _____

5   Please do not touch the _____ water or you will scald yourself. (boil)

                   _____

6 _____ milk in the morning might keep you full till lunchtime. (drink)

_____

7 I think that _____ is interesting and fun. (act)

_____

8 The victim crawled to safety, body _____ in the cold. (shiver)

_____

9 My neighbor offered _____ us mow the lawn. (help)

_____

10 When we asked the sales assistant which oven we should buy, she suggested _____ the small silver one. (buy)

_____

11 What time did you arrange _____ your friends? (meet)

_____

12 Samuel wanted _____ at the Italian restaurant on his birthday. (dine)

_____

EXERCISE 2 CONDITIONAL AND SUBJUNCTIVE MOODS

- Verbs can be used in the conditional and subjunctive mood to form sentences.
- When sentences indicate a state that will cause something to happen, they are in the conditional mood. Modal verbs like "might, could, would" are used. [Example: We might hold a year-end party. If I leave the house on time, I will not be late.]
- When sentences indicate a state that is a desire or an imaginary situation, they are in the subjunctive mood. Words like "if, I wish, I hope, I desire, I suggest, etc." are used. [Example: I hope to receive a new toy train on my birthday. If I were you, I would not do that.]

Identify whether the sentences are in the conditional (C) mood, subjunctive (S) mood or both.

1   If I were a bird, I would fly across the different continents.   _____

2   We could meet you at noon tomorrow.   _____

3   You would be the only one not going for the trip if you did not turn up.   _____

4   We hope to do our school proud by coming in first for the spelling contest.   _____

5   The supervisor requires that all the workers under him be computer literate.   _____

6   I wish we were able to spend more time helping the needy.   _____

7   If I had the time, I could watch a movie with you.   _____

8   She might be disappointed if we did not turn up for the party.   _____

9   I hope we will be taught how to start a fire when we go to the camp.   _____

10   Beautiful yellow flowers will grow on this plant if you take good care of it.   _____

POINTS /10

EXERCISE 3 — INDICATIVE, IMPERATIVE AND INTERROGATIVE MOODS

- Verbs can be used in the indicative, imperative and interrogative mood to form sentences.
- When a sentence states a fact or what is happening in reality, it is in the indicative mood. [Example: She fell during the race.]
- When a sentence gives a command, it is in the imperative mood. [Example: Open the door.]
- When a sentence asks a question, it is in the interrogative mood. [Example: Will you be at the party tomorrow?]

State whether each of the sentences are in the indicative (IN), imperative (IM) or interrogative (IG) mood.

1 The nurse risked her life to save the patients.   _____

2 Make some sandwiches for the picnic.   _____

3 Please let your mother know that I called.   _____

4 Do you have to go to school in the summer?   _____

5 The train will depart in an hour.   _____

6 Laurie yearns to visit Spain and Italy.   _____

7 Please place your shoes on the rack before you enter the house.   _____

8 Have you worked as a volunteer in Africa before?   _____

9 Which of these books would you like to read?   _____

10 Put the bait on the hook before you throw the fishing line into the sea.   _____

NAME: ....   DATE: ....

CLASS: ....

EXERCISE 4

INDICATIVE, IMPERATIVE, INTERROGATIVE, CONDITIONAL AND SUBJUNCTIVE MOODS

Use each of the verbs below to write a sentence in the given moods. You may change the form of the verb..

1 buy

(a) indicative: _____

_____

(b) interrogative: _____

_____

2 wash

(a) conditional: _____

_____

(b) imperative: _____

_____

3 read

(a) indicative: _____

_____

(b) conditional: _____

_____

(c) subjunctive: _____

_____

EXERCISE 5 — ACTIVE AND PASSIVE VOICE

- If the subject of a sentence does something, the verb is in the active voice. [Example: Peter bought a new book.]
- If something is done to the subject, the verb is in the passive voice. [Example: A new book was bought by Peter.]
- To change a sentence with a direct and indirect object from the active voice to the passive voice, use either of the objects as the subject of the sentence. Usually, the indirect object is used. [Example: Tom asked me a question. I was asked a question by Tom.] Sometimes, the subject in the sentence with the active voice is omitted. This subject can also be known as the agent. [Example: I was asked a question.]

Read each sentence and write (A) if the sentence is in the active voice and (P) if the sentence is in the passive voice.

1 The box was sealed before it was delivered. _____

2 Anna and her colleagues completed the project yesterday. _____

3 We were served our appetizer before our main course. _____

4 The tour guide took the tourists to the Golden Gate Bridge. _____

5 This dance was choreographed by a well known choreographer. _____

6 The lights in the neighborhood were turned on automatically at seven in the evening.

_____

7 I gave Alex a box of chocolates on his birthday. _____

8 The bakery sells delicious wholegrain bread. _____

9 The loose panel on the ceiling was fixed last night. _____

10 The experienced captain saved the sinking ship. _____

EXERCISE 6 — ACTIVE AND PASSIVE VOICE

In each of the following sentences, change the active voice to the passive voice. From 17 to 20, omit the "by + the original subject."

1 His mother bought the new cap.

_____

2 The carpenter made the furniture.

_____

3 The horse knocked down the lamppost.

_____

4 Mr. Freeman teaches that course.

_____

5 An experienced reporter wrote that special article.

_____

6 A thief has stolen the jewels.

_____

7 The manager himself answered the phone call.

_____

8 Weeds often choke flowers in the garden.

_____

9 Our team will win the tournament.

_____

10 A truck damaged his small car.

_____

NAME: .... DATE: ....

CLASS: ....

POINTS /10

EXERCISE **7** *ACTIVE AND PASSIVE VOICE*

In each of the following sentences, change the active voice to the passive voice. From 17 to 20, omit the "by + the original subject."

1 More and more people criticize Tommy.

_____

2 The Board of Directors is reorganizing the company.

_____

3 The clerk is typing the letter.

_____

4 The army commander is reviewing the troops.

_____

5 The editor has just rejected Shirley's manuscript.

_____

6 Old furniture filled the warehouse.

_____

7 The police are investigating the accident.

_____

8 Everyone admires good music.

_____

9 They celebrate such an occasion once a year.

_____

10 Someone has broken into the gate.

_____

NAME: .... DATE: ....

CLASS: ....

POINTS

10

EXERCISE 8 — ACTIVE AND PASSIVE VOICE

In the following sentences, change the voice, that is, active to passive and vice versa.

1 David's secretary made a report.

_____

2 Part of the city was reconstructed by the Town Council.

_____

3 Noel wrote a long letter.

_____

4 Jack has committed no crime.

_____

5 Steps should be taken to help the poor.

_____

6 We elected him captain of the team.

_____

7 Mr. Baker will give his wife a birthday present.

_____

8 A cake is being baked.

_____

9 A big fish was caught by the fisherman.

_____

10 The children eat a lot of rice.

_____

EXERCISE 9 — ACTIVE AND PASSIVE VOICE

Change the following sentences into the passive voice. Omit the agent "by + original subject."

1 You must not hammer nails into the walls.

_____

2 Farmers use cows to plow the land.

_____

3 Someone opened the back door at night.

_____

4 Someone will serve refreshments here.

_____

5 People must not leave motorcycles in the hall.

_____

6 Someone has told John to report for duty.

_____

7 They will say nothing more about the matter.

_____

8 Moles made these little hills.

_____

9 They showed us the easiest way to do it.

_____

10 Students are doing a lot of work.

_____

POINTS   / 10

EXERCISE 10   *ACTIVE AND PASSIVE VOICE*

Change the following sentences into the active voice.

1 The speed limit on this road is to be introduced by the police.

_____

2 The road to the airport is being widened by the relevant authorities.

_____

3 This noticeboard has been damaged by vandals.

_____

4 Evening gowns will be worn by all the participants.

_____

5 This rumor was started by our opponents.

_____

6 The criminal was sent to the prison by a policeman.

_____

7 All law-breakers will be punished by the authorities.

_____

8 This theory has been proved wrong by researchers.

_____

9 Some villagers were hurt by wild animals.

_____

10 It was done by Tom.

_____

POINTS /10

EXERCISE 11 SENTENCE FORMATION

- A sentence is made up of a subject and a predicate.
- The subject of a sentence refers to the person, the place or the thing that is doing something or being something. The subject of the sentence tells us who or what the sentence is about.
- Sometimes, the subject consists of one word. [Example: <u>John</u> is hungry.] Sometimes, the subject consists of more than one word. [Example: The <u>Wilma sisters</u> are famous architects. <u>Peter and Ann</u> sing very well.]
- Sometimes, there are other parts in the sentence that look like they belong to the subject but they are not part of the subject. [Example: The <u>manager</u> of the building checked every visitor with great care.]
- The predicate of the sentence refers to the verb. A verb is used to describe an action or a state of being. [Example: The birds <u>sing</u>.]
- Sometimes, the predicate consists of the verb and an adverb. [Example: The sun <u>shines</u> brightly.] Sometimes, the predicate consists of the verb together with other items like an adjective. [Example: The accident victim <u>was</u> in pain.]

In the following sentences, write the subject and the predicate. If the subject consists of several items, write the main item. If the predicate consists of several items, write the verb.

1 A good car requires constant maintenance.

S: _____

P: _____

2 Wounds caused by words are hard to cure.

S: _____

P: _____

3 All work and no play make Jack a dull boy.

S: _____

P: _____

4 Experience has taught us useful lessons.

S: _____

P: _____

5 A great fortune in the hands of a fool is a great misfortune.

S: _____

P: _____

6 The streets of some towns are known for their cleanliness.

S: _____

P: _____

7 One man's meat is another man's poison.

S: _____

P: _____

8 The country life suited me nicely.

S: _____

P: _____

9 Her mother has been teaching her the art of cooking.

S: _____

P: _____

10 William, quite pale with fright, rushed into the room.

S: _____

P: _____

POINTS /10

EXERCISE 12 — SENTENCE FORMATION

- Questions are also known as interrogative sentences.
- Questions that take "yes" or "no" answers are known as general questions. [Example: Are you a student?]
- Alternative questions are questions in which two answers are provided to indicate choice. [Example: Will you stay for dinner or leave early?]
- Informative questions are questions that ask about information. They are formed with "where, when, who, what, why, how," the auxiliary verb or modal verb, the subject and the principal verb. [Example: Where are you going?]
- Tag questions are formed by a statement and a question tag with a comma in between. If the statement is in the positive form, the question tag is negative, and vice versa. [Example: Helen is sad, isn't she?] The answer to a tag question depends on the nature of the statement. If the statement is positive, the answer is positive.

Complete each of the following sentences with a subject and a predicate.

1   The _____ singing a song on the stage _____ my sister.

2   _____ _____ _____ swimming as the weather is fine.

3   Instead of going to play, _____ _____ at home studying.

4   To tell you the truth, _____ _____ to the questions _____ totally wrong.

5   In the rain, _____ _____ _____ quickly to pick up the balls.

6   _____ _____ one of the members of the Library Club.

7   This morning, _____ _____ a letter to him.

8   Yesterday, _____ _____ John captain of our debating team.

9   _____ _____ a sparrow this morning.

10 _____ _____ _____ a tall tree.

NAME: .... DATE: ....

CLASS: ....

POINTS /10

EXERCISE 13

TYPES OF SENTENCES (Part 1)

Change the following statements into general questions.

1 Miss Smith is a good computer programmer.

_____

2 That small girl can sing very well.

_____

3 The salesman comes here every day.

_____

4 All of us enjoyed the meal very much.

_____

5 The weather is fine today.

_____

6 They seem to be intelligent students.

_____

7 She was sick yesterday.

_____

8 The bus driver has not come yet.

_____

9 Richard will be back tomorrow night.

_____

10 I realize the actual problem.

_____

POINTS

/8

EXERCISE 14   *TYPES OF SENTENCES (Part 1)*

Ask each question according to the underlined information required.

1 Mr. Cook lives in Hong Kong.

_____

2 He could come on Sunday.

_____

3 They left in the morning.

_____

4 I am going downtown.

_____

5 The workers go to work by bus.

_____

6 This book cost $20.

_____

7 It is five miles to the city.

_____

8 Jones said he would work harder next time.

_____

POINTS ⭐ /15

EXERCISE 15   TYPES OF SENTENCES (Part 1)

Ask three questions using the underlined information.

1 Peter gave me a good book last week.

(a) _____

(b) _____

(c) _____

2 Mary asked David to answer a question.

(a) _____

(b) _____

(c) _____

3 The fisherman crossed the river by boat this morning.

(a) _____

(b) _____

(c) _____

4 Henry has driven 50 miles in an hour.

(a) _____

(b) _____

(c) _____

5 They swam in the lake last Saturday.

(a) _____

(b) _____

(c) _____

EXERCISE 16 — TYPES OF SENTENCES (Part 1)

Change each of the following sentences to a question according to the type of the question indicated in parentheses.

1   All roads lead to Rome. (General)

_____

2   Tom has never been there before. (General)

_____

3   They enjoyed the meal very much. (How? Who?)

_____

4   Mrs. Brown goes shopping every Saturday afternoon. (When? What?)

_____

5   Tony painted the wall yesterday. (General)

_____

6   We can send him a letter or give him a phone call. (Alternative)

_____

7   Sam agreed to help us. (Tag question)

_____

8   Helen did not want to join us. (Tag question)

_____

9   I may start finding a job or go abroad for further studies. (Alternative)

_____

10   Some people worked mainly for the sake of money. (General)

_____

POINTS

/10

EXERCISE 17   TYPES OF SENTENCES (Part 1)

Complete each of the tag questions below.

1. She will come, _____?

2. He has seldom tried hard, _____?

3. Lily is very sad today, _____?

4. I can help you with the work, _____?

5. Mary and Susan aren't classmates, _____?

6. I laughed cheerfully, _____?

7. John doesn't like it, _____?

8. His business wasn't good last year, _____?

9. Most of us loathe dishonest people, _____?

10. You must do it now, _____?

NAME: ....   DATE: ....

CLASS: ....   POINTS   15

EXERCISE 18   *TYPES OF SENTENCES (Part 1)*

The question tags below are all wrong. Correct them.

1 She won't come today, can she?

_____

2 He is never late, was he?

_____

3 You look exhausted, aren't you?

_____

4 David made an effort to complete the work on time, doesn't he?

_____

5 You haven't said it, do you?

_____

6 You can speak English, can't you?

_____

7 We couldn't expect miracles, could you?

_____

8 I don't know how to help you, did you?

_____

9 It's a long, long journey, wasn't it?

_____

10 We have seldom been there, isn't it?

_____

11 The farmers have cleared the land for growing vegetables, didn't they?

_____

12 He will become a good sportsman, can't he?

_____

13 The clerks are working hard, don't they?

_____

14 You don't know that gentleman, isn't it?

_____

15 He can hardly expect her to help him, could you?

_____

NAME: .... DATE: ....

CLASS: ....

POINTS /6

EXERCISE 19   *IMPERATIVE SENTENCE*

- An imperative sentence is used to make a request or give an order.
- The verb used in an imperative sentence is in the present tense. The subject which is the second person "you" is often omitted. [Example: Take a seat.]
- To express the indirect order for the first or third person, begin the imperative sentence with "let." [Example: Let me take these books for you. Let the boy come in.]

Change each of the declarative sentences below into an imperative sentence.

1   You are a hardworking boy.

_____

2   Students should not play there.

_____

3   Children should not waste their time.

_____

4   Henry is a diligent student.

_____

5   Lily will tell you all about it.

_____

6   You should be careful when you do this exercise.

_____

POINTS

/6

EXERCISE 20 — EXCLAMATORY SENTENCE

- An exclamatory sentence is used to express emotional feelings like surprise, anger, etc.
- It is formed by "what" followed by a noun or "how" followed by an adjective or adverb.
  [Example: What a nice man you are! How sweetly she sings!]

Turn each of the following declarative sentences into an exclamatory sentence.

1 Our school garden is beautiful.

_____

_____

2 This young man is clever.

_____

_____

3 It is a hot day today.

_____

_____

4 These are interesting stories.

_____

_____

5 The old man has a long beard.

_____

_____

6 It is a silly question.

_____

_____

NAME: .... DATE: ....

CLASS: ....

POINTS /6

EXERCISE 21

EXCLAMATORY SENTENCE

Turn each of the following declarative sentences into an exclamatory sentence.

1 You are smart today.

_____

_____

2 These are excellent essays.

_____

_____

3 Joelle has a sweet face.

_____

_____

4 Jason is a writer. He is marvelous.

_____

_____

5 It is a wonderful feast.

_____

_____

6 Miller looks tired.

_____

_____

POINTS

/10

EXERCISE 22   *TYPES OF PHRASES*

- A phrase is a group of words that make some sense. It has no subject but it can be part of a sentence.
- A noun phrase does the work of a noun. [Example: When did you visit <u>the capital of America</u>?]
- An adjective phrase does the work of an adjective. It is usually formed with a preposition and a noun. [Example: Tom wrote a number of books <u>on language learning</u>.]
- An adverb phrase does the work of an adverb. It is often formed with a preposition and a noun. [Example: The boy ran <u>across the road</u>.]
- A present participle phrase modifies a noun. It is introduced by a present participle. [Example: This is the road <u>leading to the library</u>.]
- A past participle phrase modifies a noun. It is introduced by a past participle. [Example: <u>Drawn by one of the most famous painters of the century</u>, the painting hangs in the lobby of the museum.]

Write the phrases in the following sentences. Indicate the type in each case: adj ph, adv ph, noun ph, pres part. ph, past part. ph.

1   Many undergraduates have to work during long holidays.

_____

2   All must remain calm in the auditorium.

_____

3   Having done the work, they went home.

_____

4   An attitude of anxiety does not appeal to us.

_____

5 Getting a degree is the ultimate goal of every undergraduate.

_____

6 The village, destroyed by war, has to be rebuilt.

_____

7 The boy in front of the class is the monitor.

_____

8 Who put the vase on the bench?

_____

9 Leaving before sunrise, they reached the destination earlier.

_____

10 They followed the road leading to John's residence.

_____

POINTS /10

EXERCISE 23 TYPES OF PHRASES

- We can express the same ideas in different ways by changing the order of the words or the form of the word. [Example: The brown-eyed puppy is lost. The puppy with brown eyes is lost. Those who attend the conference will get a free tote bag. Those attending the conference will get a free tote bag. I needed help because the bag was heavy. I needed help because of the heavy bag.]

In each of the following sentences, rewrite the sentence by rewriting the underlined phrases in another way. Do not change the meaning of the sentence.

1 She did not buy the camera because the price was high.

   She did not buy the camera because of the high price.

2 The major is an honorable man.

   _____

3 The dark-haired boy is my friend's son.

   _____

4 Professor Brown is a greatly mysterious person.

   _____

5 The traveler lost his way because the fog was thick.

   _____

6 Though he was ill, he came to work as usual.

   _____

7 We are awaiting the arrival of a very important person.

   _____

8 Those who wish to take part in the competition may apply now.

   _____

9 Please make sentences with the words which are listed below.

   _____

10 Do you know the man who has a moustache?

   _____

EXERCISE **24**

DIRECT AND INDIRECT OBJECTS

- Verbs like "give, bring, take, write, send, teach, buy, etc." take a direct and an indirect object.
- A direct object answers the question "what" or "whom." An indirect object answers the question "for whom," "to whom" or "by whom." [Example: I gave Ann a book.] "Ann" is the indirect object and "book" is the direct object.
- The indirect object can be moved to the back of the sentence with the use of "to" or "for." [Example: I gave a book to Ann.]

In each of the following sentences, move the indirect object to the back of the sentence, adding "to" or "for," and vice versa.

1 Has he paid you the money?

_____

2 Mr. Lewis told us an interesting story.

_____

3 Betty made herself a new skirt.

_____

4 Mother has chosen a new handbag for Judy.

_____

5 Show your passport to the policeman.

_____

6 Can you bring a glass of water for me?

_____

7 I have just written him a long letter.

_____

8 Will you send her a Christmas card?

_____

9 He has forgotten to save the money for you.

_____

10 She cooked delicious curry for her guests.

_____

11 Mary owed him one hundred dollars.

_____

12 The airline offered a free ticket to me.

_____

13 Her mother left some food for her.

_____

14 My aunt made some cookies for us.

_____

15 Can you bring the gentleman the coffee?

_____

POINTS /15

EXERCISE 25

DIRECT AND INDIRECT OBJECTS

Change each of the following sentences so that it has "indirect object + direct object" instead of a "to" or "for" phrase.

1 Miss Smith, please bring that dictionary to me.

_____

2 Did the maid find some flowers for you?

_____

3 Don't give any sweets to the children.

_____

4 You should have offered a ride to the boy.

_____

5 He shouldn't have promised the money to that woman.

_____

6 It was very kind of her to send the message to your friend.

_____

7 They always sing some songs for the audience.

_____

8   She didn't tell any jokes to the pupils.

_____

9   Her mother wrote a letter to her every week.

_____

10 Are they bringing the books to us?

_____

11 Are you finding a job for your cousin?

_____

12 Did they give the reward to the winner?

_____

13 Has the manager promised a raise to the staff?

_____

14 Didn't they send an e-mail to you?

_____

15 Ms. Harrison made a fashionable dress for Helen.

_____

EXERCISE 26 — DIRECT AND INDIRECT SPEECH

- In direct speech, the speaker's exact words are enclosed in inverted commas or quotation marks. [Example: Jim said, "I ate one of these blueberry muffins yesterday."]
- In indirect speech or reported speech, the speaker's words are reported with structural changes made to the sentence. These include:
  (a) using the conjunction "that" to introduce the indirect speech. [Example: Jim said <u>that</u> he had eaten one of those blueberry muffins the day before.]
  (b) changing the pronoun and the possessive determiner from the first person to the second or third person. [Example: Jim said that <u>he</u> had eaten one of those blueberry muffins the day before.]
  (c) changing adverbs. [Example: Jim said that he had eaten one of <u>those</u> blueberry muffins <u>the day before</u>.]

Change each of the following direct sentences into reported, or indirect, speech.

1 "Nothing grows in my garden," she said.

_____

_____

2 "I have been in London for a month," said Bob.

_____

_____

3 "It isn't foggy today," she remarked.

_____

_____

4 "We have moved into our new apartment," said my friend.

_____

_____

5 "From the window, I can see the church," said John.

_____

_____

6 "I will go to see you as soon as I can," she replied.

_____

_____

7 "Some men make good husbands by helping in the house," Anna said.

_____

_____

8 "We don't mind working on Sundays for double pay," explained some workers.

_____

_____

9 "I'll sit up until my son returns," said Mrs. Cannon.

_____

_____

10 "I hope Tom won't be late again," said the manager.

_____

_____

NAME: .... DATE: ....

CLASS: ....

POINTS

/15

EXERCISE 27

DIRECT AND INDIRECT SPEECH

- An indirect question is introduced by the verb "asked." The question word used such as "who, what, how, where, when, etc." to ask the question should also be included in the indirect question. [Example: John asked me, "What are you doing?" John asked me what I was doing.]
- If the question does not start with a question word, use "if" or "whether" when writing the indirect question. [Example: Are you tired?" Joe asked me. Joe asked me if I was tired.]

Change each of the direct questions into indirect questions.

1 "Why are you looking out the window?" I asked him.

_____

2 "How can I do it?" she inquired.

_____

3 "What is your new car like?" I asked Sam.

_____

4 "Who owns this dictionary?" asked the teacher.

_____

5 "Where were you last night, Mr. Fagan?" she asked.

_____

6 "Have you done this sort of work before, Judy?" asked her new employer.

_____

7   "Can you read the last line on the chart?" the oculist asked me.

_____

8   "Did they really understand you?" he inquired.

_____

9   "Will you go fishing today?" Peter asked his girlfriend.

_____

10   "How far is it from here?" asked Tom.

_____

11   "Are you going to see him at the railway station?" I asked Christine.

_____

12   "Are you leaving today or tomorrow morning?" asked his secretary.

_____

13   "Do you see what I have seen, Lily?" asked the young man.

_____

14   "Do you want to go with us?" John asked Jill.

_____

15   "Shall I ask the man to wait for a while?" asked his assistant.

_____

POINTS

/10

EXERCISE 28

DIRECT AND INDIRECT SPEECH

- Indirect speech for a command or request is introduced by the verbs "order" or "request" followed by the object and the to-infinitive form of the verb. [Example: "Stop talking!" Bill said to the girl. Bill ordered the girl to stop talking.]
- We can also use "told." [Example: Bill told the girl to stop talking.]

Put each of the direct commands or requests into the reported speech.

1   "Wear sunglasses to protect your eyes from the sun," I advised the man.

_____

2   "Please pay at the counter, Madam," said the shop assistant.

_____

3   "Wash this necktie in lukewarm water, Mr. Edison," said the salesgirl.

_____

4   "Have confidence in me, boy," said the doctor.

_____

5   "Don't argue with your boss," John advised Jill.

_____

6   "Wait for me outside the post office, Tom," said the woman.

_____

7   Don't forget to feed the cat, Mary!" said her mother.

_____

8   "Write to me as often as you can," said the wife to her husband.

_____

9   "Run for your life," the man said to the small boy.

_____

10   "Please show me the way to the Palace Hotel," said the tourist.

_____

POINTS   /10

EXERCISE 29   DIRECT AND INDIRECT SPEECH

Put each of the direct commands or requests into the reported speech.

1 "Go to the canteen and get me some tea," he said to David.

_____

2 "Give way to the traffic on your right," the police officer warned us.

_____

3 "Come in through the back door," she ordered him.

_____

4 "Read the manual for instructions," the tourist guide told me.

_____

5 "Don't drive recklessly," she warned her husband.

_____

6 "Do something instead of standing there," I said to him.

_____

7 "Put on your coat before going out," she told him.

_____

8 "Watch your steps!" I warned her.

_____

9 "Tell them not to talk too much, Andy!" said the supervisor.

_____

10 "Don't swim in the pool, boys!" ordered the lifeguard.

_____

POINTS /10

EXERCISE **30** *THERE IS | THERE ARE*

- "There" is an introductory subject.
- "There is" is used to introduce a singular subject. [Example: <u>There is</u> a book on the table.]
- "There are" is used to introduce a plural subject. [Example: <u>There are</u> people in the room.]

Use 'there is' or 'there are' in front of each of the following expressions.

1 a showroom in the office

_____

2 beautiful pictures in the newspaper

_____

3 a present in the box

_____

4 two pens in the drawer

_____

5 a cabinet in the kitchen

_____

6 shops along the road

_____

7 many chairs in the classroom

_____

8 a computer on the desk

_____

9 animals on the farm

_____

10 lots of doctors in the hospital

_____

POINTS

10

EXERCISE 31

THERE IS | THERE ARE

Use "there is" or "there are" in front of each of the following expressions.

1 an unfamiliar name on the door

_____

2 several roses in the vase

_____

3 stones all over the beach

_____

4 birds in the sky

_____

5 a very interesting article in today's newspaper

_____

6 an information desk down the hall

_____

7 a pleasant elderly man in the park

_____

8 two or three letters in the mailbox

_____

9 a plane ready to take off

_____

10 only a few tourists in the art gallery

_____

NAME: ....   DATE: ....

CLASS: ....

POINTS 15

EXERCISE 32

THERE IS / THERE ARE

- Use "Is there" or "Are there" to ask questions. [Example: <u>Is there</u> any food in the refrigerator? <u>Are there</u> any students in the room?]
- Use "Is there" when referring to uncountable nouns or a singular countable noun. Use "Are there" when referring to countable nouns. [Example: <u>Is there a student</u> in the room? <u>Are there books</u> on the shelf? <u>Is there milk</u> in the carton?]
- "Any" usually goes with questions or negative statements. "Some" usually goes with positive statements. [Example: Yes, there is <u>some</u> food in the refrigerator. No, there isn't <u>any</u> food in the refrigerator.]

The question form of "there is" is "is there" and "there are" is "are there." Make a question with "Is there..." or "Are there..." with each of the following expressions. Note that "any" may be used in some questions.

1   two windows in this office

_____

2   a bottle of milk in the refrigerator

_____

3   a class this afternoon

_____

4   animals on that farm

_____

5   empty seats in the seminar room

_____

6   a road through the woods

_____

7 a portable radio that we can borrow

_____

8 old people in your family

_____

9 a good movie in town tonight

_____

10 any more important matters to be discussed

_____

11 a tree in front of your house

_____

12 good English teachers in your school

_____

13 a parade for the coming Independence Day

_____

14 many guests at the hotel

_____

15 a person here who knows Spanish well

_____

NAME: ....   DATE: ....

CLASS: ....

POINTS / 4

EXERCISE 33 — THERE IS / THERE ARE

We use "yes" in an affirmative answer. [Example: Are you tired? Yes, I am.]

Write questions for each of the set of words given and give an affirmative answer for each question.

1 students from foreign countries this year

Are there any students from foreign countries this year?

Yes, there are some students from foreign countries this year.

_____

_____

2 seats left in the auditorium

_____

_____

_____

_____

3 chances to use Japanese here

_____

_____

_____

_____

4 new words for us to learn today

_____

_____

_____

_____

NAME: .... DATE: ....

CLASS: ....

POINTS / 4

EXERCISE 34

THERE IS / THERE ARE

We use "no" in a negative answer. [Example: Was there a lucky draw after the party? No, there wasn't a lucky draw after the party.]

Write questions for each of the set of words given and give a negative answer for each question.

1 foreign visitors here last year

Were there any foreign visitors here last year? No, there were no foreign visitors here

last year.

_____

_____

2 important points in this lesson

_____

_____

_____

_____

3 outdated rules and regulations

_____

_____

_____

_____

4 serious complaints about the new tax

_____

_____

_____

_____

POINTS

/15

EXERCISE 35

THE SUBJECT-VERB AGREEMENT

- A verb in the simple present tense agrees with the subject in person and number. The singular form of the verb agrees with the singular subject. The plural form of the verb agrees with the plural subject. [Example: <u>Tom lives</u> at the end of First Street. <u>John and his wife have</u> arrived.]
- When the subject is made up of two or more inseparable elements, the elements represent a single unit and the verb is in the singular form. [Example: <u>Bread and butter</u> is a popular type of breakfast.]
- For subjects joined with "either...or" or "neither...nor," the verb matches with the subject that is closer to it. [Example: Either John or <u>Jill knows</u> the answer. Neither the book nor the <u>magazines are</u> on sale.]
- When the subject is a collective noun, the verb can be singular or plural depending on whether the subject is thought of as a whole or as individuals. [Example: The <u>committee has</u> accepted the proposal. The <u>jury have</u> not come to an agreement.]
- When the subject is an indefinite pronoun such as "everyone, someone, no one, etc.", the verb is in the singular form. [Example: <u>Nothing is</u> left undone.]
- A noun introduced with the phrase "as well as, together with, etc." does not affect the actual number of the subject before it. [Example: The <u>manager</u>, as well as his secretary, <u>has been</u> in the office the whole morning.]

Complete each sentence with a correct verb from the parentheses.

1 The horse and carriage _____ (was, were) destroyed in the fire.

2 Neither of the brothers _____ (is, are) clever.

3 To get money and not to work _____ (seems, seem) unfair to me.

4 Rubber as well as tin _____ (is, are) imported from Thailand.

5 The jury _____ (has, have) made its decision.

6 Neither Tom nor June _____ (lives, live) in this neighborhood now.

7 For those who want to join clubs, there _____ (is, are) the drama club, the skiing club, and the chess club.

8 The real meaning of 'success' for many people _____ (is, are) making more and more money.

9 The loss of a friend and a job _____ (was, were) the price Carl had to pay for his recklessness.

10 Chicken wings and chips _____ (is, are) most popular at parties.

11 Your mail along with your check _____ (has, have) reached me safely.

12 Beside the cottage _____ (stands, stand) a pine tree and a maple tree.

13 Both boys _____ (takes, take) mathematics and physics.

14 Our radio and television set _____ (is, are) getting old.

15 The food cooked by Janet _____ (tastes, taste) delicious.

EXERCISE 36 — THE SUBJECT-VERB AGREEMENT

In each of the sentences below, does the underlined verb agree with the subject? Write "Yes;" if not, write "No."

1 Every night, the mice <u>makes</u> a great deal of noise in the storeroom. _____

2 It is reported that measles <u>do not pose</u> a serious problem to mankind. _____

3 The main cause of all road accidents <u>is</u> almost the same. _____

4 After the thunderstorm, months of hard work <u>were wasted</u>. _____

5 The committee <u>has just elected</u> the new officers. _____

6 There <u>are</u> more and more tourists visiting this country. _____

7 Either of the boys <u>are allowed</u> to join the game. _____

8 Some information in the magazine <u>is</u> wrong. _____

9 Two steamships of the Neptune Shipping Company Ltd. <u>is missing</u>. _____

10 The longest version of his novels <u>have been severely criticized</u>. _____

11 New species of butterflies <u>were discovered</u> in some countries. _____

12 Chinese linguistics <u>are</u> difficult to many foreigners. _____

NAME: .... DATE: ....

CLASS: ....

POINTS /12

EXERCISE 37

THE SUBJECT-VERB AGREEMENT

In each of the sentences below, does the underlined verb agree with the subject? Write "Yes;" if not, write "No."

1   Some of your teeth <u>are decaying</u>; you must see the dentist now.   _____

2   Do you agree that the quickest means of traveling <u>are</u> by plane?   _____

3   The police inspector, with his two assistants, <u>want</u> to look into the car accident.   _____

4   Mr. Carter soon realized that athletics <u>was</u> not for him.   _____

5   She told the boss that twenty dollars <u>were</u> too little for a day's overtime work.   _____

6   Each of the rules <u>serve</u> a different purpose.   _____

7   There <u>were</u> certain moments when one would feel depressed for one reason or another.   _____

8   A lot of our office furniture <u>looks</u> worn out now.   _____

9   Either you or Jan <u>is prepared</u> to run the errand.   _____

10   Your letter as well as your books <u>have just reached</u> me.   _____

11   Even for adults, mumps <u>prove</u> serious.   _____

12   On the river bank <u>stand</u> a few tall palm trees.   _____

EXERCISE 38

THE SUBJECT-VERB AGREEMENT

In each of the sentences below, choose the correct verb from the parentheses to agree with the subject.

1 His excited reaction (reflect / reflects) the high degree of his worry.

2 That pre-school education center (consist / consists) of five teachers only.

3 The office staff often (address / addresses) the security guard as 'Officer'.

4 The host often (introduce / introduces) the audience to the songs they (prefer / prefers) singing.

5 The instructor (fix / fixes) all the rules and regulations and then (decide / decides) the training methods.

6 The teacher usually (get / gets) angry if the pupils (refuse / refuses) to be obedient.

7 Although the tests (look / looks) difficult, Jason (feel / feels) confident and unworried.

8 Peter's stay often (last / lasts) longer than expected; overstaying (make / makes) him very unpopular.

9 Among the highlights of the conference (was / were) keynote addresses by distinguished scholars.

10 What I want to do next (is / are) to temper his hard-headed approach with a soft touch.

NAME: .... DATE: ....

CLASS: ....

POINTS /10

EXERCISE 39

THE SUBJECT-VERB AGREEMENT

In each of the sentences below, choose the correct verb from the parentheses to agree with the subject.

1. Before the establishment of diplomatic relations, there (was / were) already frequent exchanges of visits between the leaders of the two countries.

2. Information Technology is one of the latest innovations that (has / have) commanded public attention.

3. Subject-verb agreement is a grammatical area which often (trouble / troubles) inexperienced English users.

4. The cactus (require/requires) less water than other plants.

5. The theme of the story (focus / focuses) on the ordeals of a self-made man.

6. The main difficulties (include / includes) traffic congestion during rush hours.

7. Neither the staff nor the director (was / were) amused by the comedian's antics.

8. The U.S. together with six other economically advanced countries (is / are) attending the Economic Summit Meeting.

9. The president, as well as his cabinet members, (was / were) among the audience.

10. There (is / are) exciting news in today's evening papers.

NAME: .... DATE: ....

CLASS: ....

POINTS

/10

EXERCISE **40** **THE SUBJECT-VERB AGREEMENT**

In each of the following sentences, check if there is any error on the subject-verb agreement. If so, correct it; if not, indicate it with "NE" (No Error).

1 The man's anger and rudeness exhibits his bad character.

exhibit

2 Pupil-centered teaching and a greater teacher-pupil rapport seem to be the latest trend.

3 The parents, as well as their only son, enjoys listening to pop songs.

4 The suspect's peculiar attitude, together with the material evidence, indicates that he was at the scene of the crime.

5 Export in the first three months of this year have substantially increased.

6 My friend's house, which used to be the shabbiest in this area, look very new now after repairing and whitewashing.

7 The suggestions made by Tony seems impracticable and unacceptable.

8 Some members of the club, partly due to their bad attitude, have become less respectable.

9 Six months is too short a period to learn a new language well.

10 Are bread and butter served daily for the children?

POINTS

/10

EXERCISE 41

THE SUBJECT-VERB AGREEMENT

In each of the following sentences, check if there is any error on the subject-verb agreement. If so, correct it; if not, indicate it with "NE" (No Error).

1. The decision which will ultimately affect one's destiny often come after careful thinking.

   comes

2. Mr. Bluce's gratitude for and devotion to the company were highly praised.

3. The cause of such protests are the instability of the economy and the uncertainty of their future.

4. Different occurrences in a person's life has an effect on his character development later.

5. The trees and plants, after the morning rain, gives off a refreshing scent.

6. The motives behind his rude behavior on the bus were not revealed.

7. The rust on the edges of the scissors have to be removed.

8. There are social and political unrest during times of war.

9. The economic development boards have agreed to develop a remote part of the country.

10. Those who work without a long-term plan is bound to fail.

POINTS

10

EXERCISE 42

PRONOUN REFERENCE

- The pronoun takes the place of the noun in the sentence. It agrees in person, number and gender with the noun referred to earlier in the context. [Example: The <u>man</u> plucked a grey hair from <u>his</u> head.]
- A subject pronoun refers to the one that the sentence is about. [Example: <u>He</u> is my brother.]
- A direct object pronoun answers the question "what" or "whom." An indirect object pronoun answers the question "for whom," "to whom" or "by whom." [Example: She helped <u>him</u> with it. Father took Tim and <u>me</u> to the theme park.]
- When another pronoun is used in the sentence to refer to an earlier indefinite pronoun, this second pronoun is usually in the singular form. [Example: <u>Someone</u> left <u>his</u> notebook on the bus.]

Fill in each blank with a correct pronoun to refer to the noun.

1   The hard-earned money will soon lose _____ value if _____ is not properly used.

2   The boy picked up a handful of sand and threw _____ into the river.

3   The pedals of the bicycle turned quickly as David pressed _____ down hard.

4   It takes some time for every foreigner to adapt _____ to local conditions.

5   Good workers do not mind engaging _____ in heavy work.

6   Some of our students are so studious that _____ devote much time to _____ books.

7   The man seems rather long-winded in _____ presentation.

8   The woman chewed on the pills as if _____ were tasty peanuts.

9   The girl tried to stop the mosquitoes from annoying _____.

10   The Browns asked the lady in the next house what _____ name was.

NAME: .... DATE: ....

CLASS: ....

POINTS /15

EXERCISE 43 PRONOUN REFERENCE

A pronoun takes the place of the noun that it is referring to. [Example: The students left their bags in the classroom. When Peter woke up in the middle of the night, he realized that no one was home.]

Fill in each blank with a correct pronoun to refer to the noun.

1 Many people often spend _____ time working for a simple living.

2 It was some time before John realized that _____ had been left without a really good friend.

3 The comforts acquired in such a manner will not last long. _____ will soon disappear.

4 Our country expects every man to do _____ duty.

5 In the modern theater, romance and realism have had _____ days.

6 All must obey the laws of _____ country.

7 Each of the distinguished writers has received _____ award.

8 If anyone cries out, the captain will punish _____.

9 None of his equipment is useful now, but _____ may be later.

10 Whoever wishes to join the game must make _____ intention known.

11 Laura is a girl _____ has great ambitions.

12 _____ do you wish to send this note to?

13 John and Jill, _____, I believe, are husband and wife, live here.

14 David and I are going to the party. _____ begins at 7 p.m.

15 I think they are plotting against _____ own students.

POINTS

/8

EXERCISE 44 — *PRONOUN REFERENCE*

- In a sentence with "neither...nor," the pronoun must match with the noun just before it. [Example: Neither Tom nor <u>Peter</u> returned <u>his</u> library before the due date.]
- In a sentence with "both" or "and," use the plural form of the pronoun. [Example: <u>Both Jane and Mary</u> take <u>their</u> pet dogs for a walk in the park every day.]

In each of the sentences, write the correct pronoun in the parentheses on the line.

1 Either Peter or John should share (their, his) dictionary with Jane.

_____

2 Both Joan and Jill have passed (her, their) examinations.

_____

3 Neither the players nor the captain wanted to do (their, his) warm-up exercise.

_____

4 Both the audience and the actors enjoyed (its, their) stage experience.

_____

5 The jury has made (their, its) decision and (they, it) will not meet again until next month.

_____

6 Either Sally or Linda will come with (his, her, their) friends tomorrow.

_____

7 Betty and Joan received (her, their) certificates from the principal.

_____

8 As Paul likes mathematics and statistics, he does well in (it, them, him).

_____

POINTS /8

EXERCISE 45 PRONOUN REFERENCE

In each of the sentences, write the correct pronoun in the parentheses on the line.

1 If you would like the Browns to come, please tell (her, him, them). _____

2 The leaders will meet here to discuss (its, their, her) plans for
the next two years. _____

3 Nobody wanted to do (their, his, its) work. _____

4 Anyone who wants to participate must produce (their, his,
its) identity card. _____

5 Everyone in the girls' choir envied (his, its, their) choir leader. _____

6 The boys said (he, she, they) would be responsible for
collecting old newspapers in (his, her, their) neighborhood. _____

7 We know full well that everybody has (his, our, its) own problems. _____

8 Anybody may kill (himself, themselves, myself) with drugs
if (he, I, they) refuses to listen to good advice. _____

POINTS

8

EXERCISE 46

PRONOUN REFERENCE

In a sentence with "each," "every," "no one" or "someone," use the singular form of the pronoun. [Example: <u>Each</u> student brings <u>his</u> own cutlery for the camp. <u>Someone</u> left <u>his</u> cellphone on the table.]

In each of the sentences, write the correct pronoun in the parentheses on the line.

1 Nobody said (it, he, they) would bring (his, its, their) radio to the picnic.   _____

2 Those attending the party said that (he, they, she) had enjoyed (himself, herself, themselves).   _____

3 Someone forgot to complete (his, its, their) form.   _____

4 Each came with (his, its, their) personal belongings.   _____

5 Mr. Brown wanted Peter and (I, me) to play for the team.   _____

6 Jack and (I, me) are the stars of the team.   _____

7 He thought others were superior to (he, him).   _____

8 Charles and (him, he) are in the same class.   _____

POINTS /20

EXERCISE 47 PRONOUN REFERENCE

Read the following passage and fill in each blank with a suitable pronoun to refer to its antecedent.

It was nearly ten o'clock. Henry was reading **1** _____ book.

2 _____ mother was sewing. Suddenly, there was a knock on the door. Henry

went to open the door. **3** _____ saw a stranger in torn clothes standing at the

doorstep. One of **4** _____ arms was bleeding.

Henry's mother told **5** _____ to let the man in and gave **6** _____

some medicine for **7** _____ wounds. The man then asked for a glass of water.

After that, **8** _____ gave **9** _____ name as 'Bob' and began to

explain things to **10** _____.

He said that **11** _____ had traveled a long way without food. The ship

12 _____ was sailing capsized and all the passengers were thrown into the

sea. Some of **13** _____ drowned; others were saved by a passing boat. Bob

was one of the people **14** _____ were saved. As the boat began to move,

Bob saw a man struggling in the sea. Bob held out **15** _____ hand and tried

to catch hold of the struggling man, and **16** _____ did. But before pulling

17 _____ up, the boat jerked and Bob fell into the sea. Luckily, a fishing boat

passed by and saved **18** _____. **19** _____ were tired and fell into

a deep sleep on the fishing boat. He awoke to find himself alone on a pier.

After hearing the story, Henry and **20** _____ mother agreed to help him

get home to his family.

EXERCISE 48   *SEQUENCE OF TENSES*

- The main clause in a sentence contains a subject and a verb and it expresses a complete thought. [Example: <u>She failed</u> because she did not work hard.]
- A subordinate clause also contains a subject and verb but it does not express a complete thought. More information is needed for the reader to make sense of the information in the subordinate clause. [Example: She failed <u>because she did not work hard</u>.]
- When the verb in the main clause is in the past tense, the verb in the subordinate clause should also be in the past tense. [Example: She <u>failed</u> because she <u>did</u> not work hard.]
- When the verb in the subordinate clause expresses a universal fact or a truth, the tense remains in the present tense. [Example: Who discovered that the earth <u>goes</u> around the sun?]
- When comparison is being made, any appropriate tense will do. [Example: Sam liked you better than he <u>likes</u> me.]
- When the verb in the main clause is in the present tense, the verb in the subordinate clause can be in the present tense or other suitable tenses. [Example: Mary <u>believes</u> that she <u>will pass</u> the test. The manager <u>has told</u> us that he <u>was</u> ill yesterday.]

In each of the following sentences, fill in the blank with the correct form of the given verb in parentheses at the end of the sentence.

1   Janet is not as active as she _____ three years ago. (be)

2   I understand that you _____ in this university for three years. (study)

3   When the rain was over, they _____ out to play. (go)

4   His health has deteriorated since he _____ last year. (retire)

5   Whenever he _____, the people gathered to listen to him. (speak)

6   She told me that she _____ it if she could. (do)

7 You may sit wherever you _____ (like)

8 As soon as he heard the news, he _____ to me. (write)

9 When the customs officer checked my suitcase, I _____ on. (look)

10 When she got home, it _____ (rain)

11 While he was eating his lunch, someone _____ (call)

12 She reached the railway station after she _____ for thirty minutes. (walk)

13 If you don't go to the stall soon, everything _____ (sell) out.

14 She did not buy the new car until she _____ the old one. (dispose of)

15 He would pass if he _____ harder. (work)

EXERCISE 49

SEQUENCE OF TENSES

In each of the sentences, correct the wrong tense sequence or the wrong verb form.

1 The forsaken house became derelict and eventually falling down.

_____

_____

2 My brother stuffed his clothes into the suitcase and then hurrying off.

_____

_____

3 Some believe that this tonic drink could relieve tension and increases thinking power.

_____

_____

4 At least two students from this class have been selected for the tennis match and the rest had been selected for the basketball game.

_____

_____

5 This medicine is not harmful if the patient followed doctor's directions properly.

_____

_____

POINTS

/10

EXERCISE 50 SEQUENCE OF TENSES

In each of the sentences, correct the wrong tense sequence or the wrong verb form.

1 The accident would not have happened if proper precautions have been taken.

_____

2 The university's school of education thinks that Julia is not too young to be trained if she really focused on becoming a teacher.

_____

3 These new appliances would only be used when we move to the new house next month.

_____

4 When the police inspector noticed that the policeman in charge does not report back, he investigated the matter himself.

_____

5 The sooner the people get out of their complacency the better it would be for the company as a whole.

_____

6 The actress did not really imply that she is displeased with her performance.

_____

7 I told Betty if she had tried harder, she would succeed.

_____

8 Some people think that Napoleon's main hope in conquering Italy was that he can win the praise of Josephine.

_____

9 By the time the new crop was ready, the barns are almost empty.

_____

10 When his army lost, he felt that life is no longer worth living.

_____

POINTS

10

EXERCISE **51**

SEQUENCE OF TENSES

In each of the sentences, correct the wrong tense sequence or the wrong verb form.

1 When the teacher told the students about the surprise quiz, all the students groan in protest.

_____

2 Some recent seminars on the future of human beings, which I attended, pointed out that the destruction of the human race is possible.

_____

3 Do you think that, as he was ill yesterday, he isn't going to tomorrow's meeting?

_____

4 When Tom sees the poor grade on his test paper, he walked out of the class in silence.

_____

5 Heavy fighting involving tanks and rockets has broken out between the two countries, military sources said yesterday.

_____

6 I went to the United States in 1999, but I did not stay there long and return shortly.

_____

7 The thief hit the man, took his money, opened the door, and running away at high speed.

_____

8 The old man told the court that the thief had broken into his house three times and he will tremble each time he heard noises outside his door.

_____

9 The police ordered an investigation into the case of a foreign woman who was a housewife but ending up committing major crimes.

_____

10 I saw a number of healthy and strong people, aged from 30 to 40, begging in busy streets. They approached passersby and saying, 'We need a job. Could you help us?'

_____

NAME: ....   DATE: ....

CLASS: ....

POINTS

/7

EXERCISE 52   *FUNCTIONS OF INFINITIVES*

- The infinitive can be used as the subject of a sentence. [Example: <u>To learn a foreign language</u> takes time.]
- The infinitive can be used as the object of a sentence. [Example: I want <u>to help him</u>.]
- The infinitive can be used as the complement of the verb. This means that the infinitive is the object of another verb. [Example: The security guard told the rowdy group <u>to leave</u>.]
- The infinitive can also be used without the word "to." [Example: I saw the man <u>jump</u> into the river. Nobody can <u>enter</u> this place before ten.]
- We can combine sentences using the infinitive. [Example: My brother cleaned his room. My mother told him. My mother told my brother to clean his room.]
- We can also replace an adjective clause with the infinitive. [Example: Jim was the only one who heard the noise. Jim was the only one to hear the noise.]

Combine each pair of sentences by using the infinitive.

1   He collects old coins. This is his hobby.

_____

2   The gardener planted the rose bushes. His employer requested it.

_____

3   The child is crying. Did you hear it?

_____

4   Every basketball team has a coach. He directs the players.

_____

5   You must let go of your insecurities. You can perform better this way.

_____

6   Every citizen should do his duties. The country expects this of every person.

_____

7   He has risen to eminence from obscurity. It is highly creditable for him.

_____

EXERCISE **53** *FUNCTIONS OF INFINITIVES*

Combine each pair of sentences by using the infinitive.

1 I teach. This is my job.

_____

2 He is buying the paint. He wants to paint the doors.

_____

3 The firemen rushed into the house. They wanted to save the residents.

_____

4 They got up very early. They wanted to catch the first bus.

_____

5 John is going to America. He wants to embark on science research.

_____

6 The businessman changed his phone number. He wanted to avoid strangers' calls.

_____

7 He has a big box. He plans to put old letters in it.

_____

EXERCISE 54 — FUNCTIONS OF INFINITIVES

We can use the infinitive to change the way a sentence is written without changing the meaning of the sentence. [Example: My mother was surprised when she saw me home so early. My mother was surprised to see me home so early.]

In each of the following sentences, replace the underlined words with an infinitive or infinitive phrase.

1 Tom was the first person <u>who arrived here</u>.

_____

2 The captain was the last person <u>who left the sinking ship</u>.

_____

3 There are a lot of mistakes <u>that must be corrected</u>.

_____

4 I was surprised <u>when I heard the news</u>.

_____

5 It is better <u>that we hear it from you</u>.

_____

NAME: .... DATE: ....

CLASS: ....

EXERCISE 55 — FUNCTIONS OF INFINITIVES

In each of the following sentences, replace the underlined words by an infinitive or infinitive phrase.

1 If he had another child <u>whom he could talk to</u>, he would be happier.

_____

2 It is necessary <u>that everyone should know the facts</u>.

_____

3 John was the only one <u>who realized the danger</u>.

_____

4 It is advisable <u>that we go out one by one</u>.

_____

5 I don't want to go to the wedding dinner because I have nothing special <u>that I can wear</u>.

_____

6 I want a quiet place <u>where I can study</u>.

_____

7 Would you be kind <u>and lend me your car</u>?

_____

8 Danny was the first person <u>who had visited that deserted island</u>.

_____

9 I really don't know how <u>I can do it</u>.

_____

10 I was glad <u>that I knew her</u>.

_____

NAME: .... DATE: ....

CLASS: ....

POINTS

/8

EXERCISE 56 FUNCTIONS OF GERUNDS

- A gerund is marked by "-ing." It can function as a subject. [Example: <u>Reading</u> is a good hobby.]
- It can also function as an object. [Example: I don't remember having said it. Jason was interested in <u>doing the work assigned</u>.]
- It can also be a complement of a verb. [Example: Joe's pastime is <u>taking photos</u>.]
- The gerund is usually used after the verbs "stop, enjoy, go, mind, etc." [Example: They enjoyed <u>reading novels</u>.]

Put each of the verbs in the parentheses into the gerund.

1 Stop _____ (argue) and start _____. (work)

2 She prefers _____ (sleep) in an air-conditioned room.

3 I suggest _____ (hold) another meeting next week.

4 Professor Dunlop finished _____ (speak) and sat down.

5 Tony was fined for _____ (drive) without a license.

6 If you can't turn the key, try _____ (put) some oil in the lock.

7 You must seize the opportunity of _____ (help) your classmates.

8 Can you make a cake without _____ (use) eggs?

NAME: .... DATE: ....

CLASS: ....

POINTS /10

EXERCISE 57   *FUNCTIONS OF GERUNDS*

Put each of the verbs in the brackets into the gerund.

1. The thief escaped by _____ (jump) out of the window.

2. Don't risk _____ (lose) your money in an investment you are unsure of.

3. Imagine _____ (live) with someone talkative.

4. Do you enjoy _____ (fish) in the river?

5. Would you mind _____ (lend) me some money?

6. The government has a plan for _____ (attract) foreign investors.

7. Betty does not feel like _____ (eat) today.

8. I hate to see people _____ (bully) the weak or the poor.

9. Do you remember _____ (watch) the film show together?

10. What about _____ (go) to the movie tonight?

NAME: .... DATE: ....

CLASS: ....

EXERCISE **58** *FUNCTIONS OF GERUNDS*

- Some verbs are only followed by the infinitive. [Example: I don't <u>expect to find</u> him here.]
- Some verbs are only followed by the gerund. [Example: The boy <u>admitted being</u> careless.]
- Some verbs can be followed by the gerund or the infinitive. [Example: You must <u>try to help</u> him. / You must <u>try helping</u> him.]

In each of the following blanks, put the given verb into either the infinitive or the gerund .

1 The teacher urged the pupils _____ (work) harder.

2 I wish _____ (see) the officer-in-charge now.

3 The mechanic warned her not _____ (touch) the wires.

4 Don't forget _____ (lock) the door before _____ (go) out.

5 Mrs. Cook told her daughter _____ (beware) of strangers.

6 He annoyed us by _____ (smoke).

7 All are expected _____ (obey) the rules and regulations.

8 The thief decided _____ (disguise) himself by _____ (dress) as a woman.

EXERCISE **59**

FUNCTIONS OF GERUNDS

In each of the following blanks, put the given verb into either the infinitive or the gerund .

1 I am prepared _____ (wait) here.

2 The driver was fined for _____ (speed).

3 I regret _____ (inform) you that your application has not been successful.

4 We could not help _____ (laugh) at the clown's funny performance.

5 Those dirty clothes need _____ (clean).

6 The doctor advised the patient _____ (play) more outdoor games.

7 The man keeps _____ (forget) _____ (wind) the alarm clock.

8 She hates _____ (answer) the phone and often lets it _____ (ring).

NAME: .... DATE: ....

CLASS: ....

POINTS

/8

EXERCISE 60   *FUNCTIONS OF GERUNDS*

In each of the following blanks, put the given verb into either the infinitive or the gerund .

1 She wants her daughter _____ (go) to a dentist.

2 A technician will come _____ (show) us how _____ (use) the new machine.

3 I have no intention of _____ (visit) that place again, so don't ask me.

4 Some people seem _____ (have) great fondness for _____ (argue).

5 You will have _____ (wait) till the rain stops.

6 He postponed _____ (make) a quick decision.

7 The merchant made a lot of money by _____ (sell) jewels.

8 Imagine _____ (have) _____ (wake) up at 4.30 a.m.!

EXERCISE 61 — LESS OFTEN USED 'CONTINUOUS TENSES'

- The present perfect continuous tense is used for an action which started in the past and is still continuing. [Example: He has been teaching in this school since 2000.]
- It is formed by the auxiliary verb "have/has," been and the present participle. [Example: I have been writing the whole afternoon.]
- The interrogative form of the tense is formed by moving the auxiliary verb "have/has" to the front of the subject. [Example: Have you been waiting a long time?]
- The past perfect continuous tense is used for an action which started and continued before the other past action began. [Example: We were told that some workers had not been working for many days.]
- It is formed with "had been" and the present participle. [Example: I had not been working.]
- The future perfect continuous tense is used to show a future action which will start and continue in the future. [Example: We will have been working for two hours before her arrival.]
- It is formed with "shall/will," have been and the present participle. [Example: I shall have been working here for exactly one month at the end of this week.]

Complete each sentence with the given verb in the correct tense.

1   Tom _____ me. (just meet)

2   Henry _____ this set of furniture for ten years. (possess)

3   It _____ (rain). As a matter of fact, it _____ since early this morning. (rain)

4   The earth _____ round the sun. (go)

5   When I _____ (reach) home, Mother _____ (finish) cooking.

6   I _____ (see) my pen as soon as I _____ (enter) the room.

7   The cat _____ (bite) the boy when he _____ (walk) in the field.

8   After I _____ (eat) my breakfast, I _____ (go) to office.

9   I _____ (watch) television for two hours when the telephone rang.

10   Before the police arrived, the thief _____ (leave) the house.

11   By that time, then, I _____ (sleep).

12   By next year, David _____ (live) here for 20 years.

NAME: .... DATE: ....

CLASS: ....

POINTS

/10

EXERCISE 62   TYPES OF SENTENCES (Part 2)

- The subject of a sentence refers to the person, the place or the thing that is doing something or being something. [Example: <u>Birds</u> fly.]
- The predicate of the sentence refers to the verb and other words such as an adverb or an adjective. [Example: The sun <u>gives light</u>.]

In each of the following sentences, pick out the subject (indicated by "S") and the predicate (indicated by "P").

1 He laughs.

_____

2 Several men helped the woman.

_____

3 This country has changed a lot.

_____

4 The rain stopped at two o'clock.

_____

5 I told him to send those letters.

_____

6 The film at the theater was very exciting.

_____

7 Mr. Dickens teaches English.

_____

8 The pupils are working hard.

_____

9 Some old buildings have been demolished.

_____

10 I am a lecturer.

_____

POINTS / 10

EXERCISE 63 — TYPES OF SENTENCES (Part 2)

In each of the following sentences, pick out the subject (indicated by "S") and the predicate (indicated by "P").

1 June is a typist.

_____

2 It has two legs.

_____

3 A man and a woman were injured in a car accident.

_____

4 John and I are next-door neighbors.

_____

5 A woman with a stroller is walking along a lake.

_____

6 The girls as well as the boy have been scolded.

_____

7 John is the man to work with.

_____

8 The man standing on the platform is a lecturer.

_____

9 Dr. Forster is a man of great ability.

_____

10 We did not have much confidence in him.

_____

EXERCISE 64 TYPES OF SENTENCES (Part 2)

- An imperative sentence is used to make a request or give an order.
- The verb used in an imperative sentence is in the present tense. The subject which is the second person "you" is often omitted. [Example: Come here!]
- An exclamatory sentence is used to express emotional feelings like surprise, anger, etc.
- It is formed by "what" followed by a noun or "how" followed by an adjective or adverb. [Example: What a beautiful dress! How peaceful the countryside is!]

Change questions 1-3 to exclamatory sentences and questions 4-5 to imperative sentences.

1 The young man is clever.

_____

_____

2 It is cold.

_____

_____

3 The baby cries loudly.

_____

_____

4 You must close the door behind you.

_____

_____

5 Helen will tell him about it.

_____

_____

EXERCISE 65

TYPES OF SENTENCES (Part 3)

- A simple sentence can be divided into the subject which is the noun or pronoun and the predicate which is the rest of the sentence. [Example: Rumors are often false.]
- A compound sentence consists of two or more sentences joined by a coordinating conjunction "and, or, but, so, for, etc." Both sentences are equally important. [Example: Rain suddenly came and we all got wet.]
- A complex sentence consists of a main clause and one or more subordinate clauses. The main clause expresses a complete thought. [Example: <u>The boxes toppled</u> because they were not properly stacked.]
- A subordinate clause does not express a complete thought. More information is needed to understand the clause. [Example: She failed <u>because she did not work hard</u>.]
- The subordinate clause can be a noun clause (does the job of a noun), an adjective clause (does the job of an adjective) or an adverb clause (does the job of an adverb)
- Noun clause: James said <u>that he could not come tonight</u>.
- Adjective clause: Do you know the lady <u>who is talking to Lily</u>?
- Adverb clause: She could not come <u>because she was busy</u>.

In each of the following sentences, indicate whether it is a simple, compound or complex sentence.

1 Although few of the actors had experience, they performed quite well.

_____

2 I want all of you to return to your seats now.

_____

3 Do not be discouraged by difficulties, which will occur from time to time.

_____

4 Go to the library and meet me at the entrance.

_____

5 When I first read that magazine, I found it hard to understand.

_____

6 Birds fly, but fish swim.

_____

7 During the 1930s, the whole world was in bad shape.

_____

8 If you have not done your homework, don't go out to play.

_____

9 They danced and they sang at the same time.

_____

10 In spite of the bad weather, the football game went on.

_____

POINTS /10

EXERCISE **66**   *TYPES OF SENTENCES (Part 3)*

- A noun clause is often introduced by the conjunction "that." It can be the subject of the sentence. [Example: <u>That she is not injured</u> is fortunate.]
- It can also be the object of the transitive verb in the main clause. [Example: Nancy insisted <u>that she was right</u>.]
- It can be the subjective complement of the linking verb "is." [Example: The fact is <u>that most students are exam-oriented</u>.]
- It can be the objective complement. [Example: I am sure <u>that everything will be fine in the end</u>.] The word "that" can be omitted as well. [Example: Nancy insisted <u>she was right</u>.]
- It can be in apposition to the noun. An appositive renames a noun that is right next to it. [Example: You assumption <u>that all will be fine</u> is not valid.]
- A noun clause can be the object of the preposition. [Example: We often judge people by <u>what they do</u>.]

In each of the following sentences, write the noun clause on the line and indicate its function.

1   How long I shall stay here is uncertain.

_____

2   It was reported that the king was murdered.

_____

3   The truth is that the poor are often ill-treated.

_____

4   It is clear that the driver was guilty.

_____

5   We know what it is about.

_____

6 Who will come is no concern of ours.

_____

7 I stick to what I have promised to do.

_____

8 The doctor came to the conclusion that the patient was out of danger.

_____

9 Please tell me what his name is.

_____

10 That Texas is a big state is an undeniable fact.

_____

NAME: .... DATE: ....

CLASS: ....

POINTS

/10

EXERCISE 67 — *TYPES OF SENTENCES (Part 3)*

- An indirect question is a sentence that asks a question but ends with a period. [Example: She asked me where I was last night.]
- A noun clause in an indirect question is introduced by the question word followed by the subject and verb. [Example: I want to know where he is.] In general indirect questions, the noun clause is introduced by "whether" or "if." [Example: I want to know <u>whether you can go for the party</u>.]

Complete each sentence with a noun clause in the form of an indirect question.

1 What time is it?

I have no idea _____.

2 How well does he speak English?

I don't know _____.

3 When was this school built?

I don't remember _____.

4 How many children does he have?

He hasn't told me _____.

5 Where will you spend your vacation?

I haven't decided _____.

6 How much money are we going to need?

I haven't figured out _____.

7 Do you know the location of the neighborhood U.S. Post Office?

Please tell me _____.

8 Can cats see at night?

I wonder _____.

9 Why did you go to that kind of place?

Mrs. Smith asked her son _____.

10 Will you go shopping with me, Jenny?

Jim asked Jenny _____.

POINTS /5

EXERCISE 68   *TYPES OF SENTENCES (Part 3)*

An adjective clause is introduced by a relative pronoun such as "who, which, that, whose, etc." or a relative adverb "why, when or where." The adjective clause will modify a noun. The noun it modifies is known as the "antecedent." [Example: A doctor is a person <u>who cures patients</u>. Jason's latest book, <u>which came out last month</u>, has been a great success.]

Write the adjective clause on the lines below the sentence and circle the antecedent it modifies.

1   The time when the plane leaves cannot be changed.

_____

_____

2   The house where the fire broke out was surrounded by the police.

_____

_____

3   It was the rain that caused the match to be canceled.

_____

_____

4   The person who climbs the fastest is sure to win.

_____

_____

5   It is a long lane that has no turning.

_____

_____

POINTS / 5

EXERCISE 69 **TYPES OF SENTENCES (Part 3)**

Complete each sentence with a suitable adjective clause.

1 The house _____

_____ was sold last month.

2 We went to the movie _____

_____.

3 This letter is from my brother, _____

_____.

4 I am prepared to accept anything _____

_____.

5 His father, _____

_____, intends to retire soon.

EXERCISE 70 — TYPES OF SENTENCES (Part 3)

Combine the sentences so that it contains an adjective clause.

1 Tony had been driving all day. He was tired and wanted to sleep.

_____

_____

2 This is Mrs. Jones. Her son won the championship last year.

_____

_____

3 Mr. Smith said he was too busy to see me. I had come especially to see him.

_____

_____

4 The thief has been caught. He tried to break into the shop.

_____

_____

5 The book belongs to John. It is in the bookcase.

_____

_____

POINTS /5

EXERCISE 71   **TYPES OF SENTENCES (Part 3)**

Join the sentences using an adjective clause.

1 I met Mary. She asked me to give you this booklet.

_____

_____

2 His boss doesn't procrastinate. He heard what the matter was and wasn't sympathetic.

_____

_____

3 I don't know the man. His car was damaged in a road accident.

_____

_____

4 You sent me a present. Thank you very much.

_____

_____

5 The bed has no mattress. I sleep on it.

_____

_____

POINTS

10

EXERCISE 72   *TYPES OF SENTENCES (Part 3)*

- An adverb clause is introduced by a subordinating conjunction such as "when, since, before, after or while." These conjunctions show time. [Example: He had done the work <u>before his father came home</u>.]
- It can also be introduced with "because, since, as, now that" to show reason. [Example: Tom did not come <u>because he was ill</u>.]
- It can also be introduced with "if, unless." [Example: <u>If you don't understand</u>, please ask again.]
- It can be introduced using "although, though." [Example: <u>Although he is rich</u>, he is not arrogant.]
- It can also be introduced using "where, wherever, so that, in order that, so…that, as… as, than, as, as if." [Example: I did <u>as I was told</u>.]

In each of the following sentences, write the adverb clause on the line and indicate its kind.

1   If I were you, I would not do such a thing.

_____

2   Henry speaks better than he writes.

_____

3   We will go to the restaurant where the famous chef works.

_____

4   He studies so that he may pass the test.

_____

5   Come if you wish.

_____

6 Though it is raining, he still comes to see me.

_____

7 Since he repented, we could let him go.

_____

8 When he heard the news, he wrote to me about it.

_____

9 Jane was so frightened that she could not utter a word.

_____

10 You may fail unless you work very hard.

_____

NAME: .... DATE: ....

CLASS: ....

POINTS /8

EXERCISE 73 TYPES OF SENTENCES (Part 3)

Answer each of the questions with an adverb clause. Use the given information in the parentheses.

1 When did he want to borrow money from you? (he came to work)

_____

2 Why did he want to borrow money from you? (he lost his wallet)

_____

3 How long has Tom been asking you for favors? (I knew him)

_____

4 When will you move? (I can find a new house)

_____

5 Where can you meet me? (it is convenient for you)

_____

6 When did she buy her car? (she had come back from Europe)

_____

7 Why didn't John wear a coat? (he didn't know it was cold)

_____

8 How long has she been interested in painting? (she was a small girl)

_____

POINTS

/8

EXERCISE **74** 'IT' AS AN INTRODUCTORY SUBJECT TO REPRESENT TO-INFINITIVE / PHRASE

"It" can be used as an introductory subject. The subject of the sentence is shifted to the end of the sentence and introduced using the "to-infinitive/phrase." [Example: <u>It</u> is unusual for Brenda <u>to be late for a meeting</u>.]

Use "It" and the given words to make a sentence in this pattern: "It + Be +Adj / Noun + to-infinitive / phrase," as in the example above.

1 necessary - return the books to the library

_____

2 foolish - quarrel with friends

_____

3 a shame - tell lies to friends

_____

4 hard - learn by heart all the new words

_____

5 comfortable - sit on a sofa watching TV

_____

6 fun - talk about interesting activities

_____

7 useless - explain such a thing to her

_____

8 helpful - repeat the sentence loudly

_____

NAME: .... DATE: ....

CLASS: .... **POINTS** /8

EXERCISE 75 — 'IT' AS AN INTRODUCTORY SUBJECT TO REPRESENT TO-INFINITIVE / PHRASE

Use "It" and the given words to make a sentence in this pattern: "It + Be + Adj / Noun + to-infinitive / phrase."

1 a good idea - get away from the crowded city

_____

2 a pleasure - come to know you

_____

3 tiring - swim against the stream

_____

4 wonderful - visit such a nice place

_____

5 a relief - learn that he returned safe and sound

_____

6 dangerous - drive fast on a rainy day

_____

7 difficult - cross the street during the busy time

_____

8 harmful - read by a weak light

_____

EXERCISE 76 'IT' AS AN INTRODUCTORY SUBJECT TO REPRESENT GERUND / GERUND PHRASES

"It" can be used as an introductory subject, taking the place of a gerund or a gerund phrase. The gerund or gerund phrase is then shifted to the end of the sentence. [Example: It is fun playing games with children.]

Rewrite each of the sentences by using "It" as a sentence introducer.

1 Speaking too fast is distracting.

_____

_____

2 Pretending to be smart is no good.

_____

_____

3 Talking to such a person is no use.

_____

_____

4 Learning a foreign language is worthwhile.

_____

_____

5 Reading storybooks is real fun.

_____

_____

NAME: ....   DATE: ....

CLASS: ....   POINTS   5

EXERCISE 77   **'IT' AS AN INTRODUCTORY SUBJECT TO REPRESENT GERUND / GERUND PHRASES**

Rewrite each of the sentences by using "It" as a sentence introducer.

1 Teaching foreigners to write Chinese is a difficult job.

_____

_____

2 Losing your temper with her is useless.

_____

_____

3 Asking him that question again is pointless.

_____

_____

4 Getting on a crowded bus with a heavy box is hard.

_____

_____

5 Getting along with those colleagues seems impossible.

_____

_____

POINTS /5

EXERCISE 78 'IT' AS AN INTRODUCTORY OBJECT TO REPLACE AN INFINITIVE PHRASE OR GERUND PHRASE

"It" can be used as an introductory object, taking the place of a gerund phrase or an infinitive phrase. The phrase is then shifted to the end of the sentence. [Example: We consider it our duty to defend our country. He did not consider it worthwhile spending too much time playing.]

Answer each question with the given words. Use "It" as an introductory object.

1 What do you consider your duty? (to teach the young)

_____

_____

2 What did you think was best? (not to stay out late tonight)

_____

_____

3 What did he find embarrassing? (to be among the women)

_____

_____

4 What did the plan make possible? (for young people to be vocationally trained)

_____

_____

5 What do you feel is good? (spreading education among the young)

_____

_____

POINTS /5

EXERCISE 79

'IT' AS AN INTRODUCTORY OBJECT TO REPLACE AN INFINITIVE PHRASE OR GERUND PHRASE

Rewrite each of the sentences by using "It" as a sentence introducer.

1 What do you imagine is desirable? (for everyone to be able to go to university)

_____

_____

2 What did he find troublesome? (having to go through so much red tape)

_____

_____

3 What does the manager think is possible? (to do everything at short notice)

_____

_____

4 What do you consider pointless? (recovering lost time)

_____

_____

5 What does she think is worthwhile? (doing everything perfectly well)

_____

_____

NAME: .... DATE: ....

CLASS: ....

POINTS / 6

EXERCISE 80 THE INVERTED ORDER

"So" is used to respond in the affirmative. The subject verb order is inverted. [Example: Jack likes strawberries. So do I.]

The inverted answer with "so" is to agree in the affirmative. Respond to each of the sentences with the given word(s). Be sure to invert the answer with "so."

1 Mary walks to school. (I)

_____

_____

2 John is hungry now. (Helen)

_____

_____

3 The boys will help us. (the girls)

_____

_____

4 Jim is reading a storybook. (his sister)

_____

_____

5 Jack would like some more tea. (I)

_____

_____

6 They were surprised. (Richard)

_____

_____

EXERCISE **81**   *THE INVERTED ORDER*

The inverted answer with "so" is to agree in the affirmative. Respond to each of the sentences with the word(s) given in parentheses. Be sure to invert the answer with "so."

1 Peggie can command the workers well. (Jason)

_____

_____

2 Helen has seen the pictures. (her friends)

_____

_____

3 Christine may resign one of these days. (Shoba)

_____

_____

4 John works in a big bank. (his elder brother)

_____

_____

5 I am expecting an important letter today. (Simon)

_____

_____

6 Butter is made from milk. (cheese)

_____

_____

NAME: .... DATE: ....

CLASS: ....

POINTS /5

EXERCISE 82 *THE INVERTED ORDER*

"Neither/Nor" is used to provide a negative response. The subject verb order is inverted.
[Example: The apples are not sweet. Neither are the oranges. She can't cycle. Nor can I.]

The inverted answer with "neither / nor" is to agree in the negative. Respond to each of the sentences with the word(s) given in parentheses. Be sure to invert the answer with "neither / nor."

1 The doors weren't open. (the windows)

_____

_____

2 Mary isn't coming with us. (Linda)

_____

_____

3 Orange trees don't grow here. (peach trees)

_____

_____

4 Jason can't go to the party. (John)

_____

_____

5 The opera wasn't very interesting. (the concert)

_____

_____

NAME: .... DATE: ....

CLASS: ....

POINTS

5

EXERCISE 83

THE INVERTED ORDER

The inverted answer with "neither / nor" is to agree in the negative. Respond to each of the sentences with the given word(s). Be sure to invert the answer with "neither / nor."

1 Cats are not allowed on the plane. (birds)

_____

_____

2 The Browns won't be here for Christmas. (Mr. and Mrs. Brown)

_____

_____

3 The children weren't tired at all. (the parents)

_____

_____

4 The public didn't welcome the new policy. (political critics)

_____

_____

5 Cows don't like milk. (rabbits)

_____

_____

POINTS /6

EXERCISE **84** ABSOLUTE CONSTRUCTION

An absolute construction is an independent participle phrase with a subject of its own. It can be formed by using "being" or "having" after the subject. [Example: <u>It being a fine day</u>, we went swimming. <u>The weather being good</u>, we went for a picnic.]

Join each pair of sentences together with an absolute construction consisting of "being" or "having."

1 The weather was fine. They went fishing.

_____

_____

2 The boat sprang a leak. The captain asked for rescue.

_____

_____

3 The theater was full. All late-comers were sent away.

_____

_____

4 The rain stopped. The workers resumed work.

_____

_____

5 The day was hot. We took off our coats.

_____

_____

6 Everyone arrived. The game began.

_____

_____

EXERCISE 85   *ABSOLUTE CONSTRUCTION*

Join each pair of sentences together with an absolute construction consisting of 'being' or 'having'.

1   All the seas were rough. No fishermen went out.

_____

_____

2   The musical concert was over. The audience left.

_____

_____

3   It is a new school. All the facilities are in good condition.

_____

_____

4   They have done their work. They went home.

_____

_____

5   The sun came out. They resumed their work.

_____

_____

6   Time permits. I will redo the assignment.

_____

_____

POINTS /10

EXERCISE 86 **ORDER OF ADJECTIVES IN A SENTENCE**

When two or more adjectives are used in a sentence, they should be arranged in a logical way: determiners, possessives, ordinals, numbers, adjectives of quality, size, shape, length, colors, nations and attributive nouns. [Example: Mary likes that girl's <u>white flurry stuffed</u> rabbit.]

Complete each sentence by arranging the given adjectives in parentheses in logical order.

1   There is _____ equipment in this factory.
    (iron, some, expensive, black)

2   What _____ morning it is!
    (a, uncomfortable, rainy, cold)

3   Mrs. Lee likes to drink _____ juice.
    (Italian, red, grape, sweet)

4   There are _____ chairs in the living room.
    (white, square, some, comfortable)

5   Jason has just written _____ storybook.
    (an, amusing, Spanish, easy-to-read)

6   My friend is a _____, _____ man. (optimistic, nice)

7   The farmer and his family live in a hut which is _____, _____, and
    _____. (shabby, dark, old)

8   The invited guest gave a _____, _____, and _____ speech.
    (unstimulating, long-winded, dull)

9   It will do an employee good to be _____, _____, and _____ to the
    company to which he belongs. (dedicated, tactful, industrious)

10 Whoever is _____, _____, and _____ will lead a happy life.
    (joyous, broad-minded, generous)

NAME: .... DATE: ....

CLASS: ....

EXERCISE 87

SYNTHESIS OF SENTENCES

We use "and" or "but" to join two independent clauses. "But" is used to show a contrast in ideas. "And" is used to express two similar thoughts or to show the sequence of events. [Example: She was exhausted, <u>but</u> she refused to take a break from her chores. He climbed up the slope, <u>and</u> stopped to rest at the top.]

Combine each pair of sentences by using the coordinating conjunction "and" or "but."

1 Lily was the monitor last year. She is not the monitor this year.

_____

_____

2 She is clever. She works hard.

_____

_____

3 He is intelligent. He is not hardworking.

_____

_____

4 The woman looked everywhere. She could not find her kitten.

_____

POINTS

/4

EXERCISE 88

SYNTHESIS OF SENTENCES

Combine each pair of sentences by using the coordinating conjunction "and" or "but."

1   I shouted for John. He could not hear me.

_____

_____

2   They are going to the beach. They have asked me to join them.

_____

_____

3   Joelle borrowed a book from the library. She enjoyed reading it.

_____

_____

4   Tom bought a new book. It was too difficult to understand.

_____

_____

POINTS /4

EXERCISE 89 **SYNTHESIS OF SENTENCES**

We can use the correlative conjunctions "either...or" and "neither...nor" to join sentences. [Example: Jim wants to play basketball. Jim wants to play football. Jim wants to play either basketball or football. The books are not cheap. The books are not interesting. The books are neither cheap nor interesting.]

Combine each pair of sentences by using the correlative conjunction "either...or" or "neither...nor."

1 I can play table tennis. I can play basketball.

_____

_____

2 That school is not new. It is not well-known, either.

_____

_____

3 Tom is not intelligent. He is not hardworking, either.

_____

_____

4 The jewels may be lost. They may be stolen.

_____

_____

POINTS / 4

EXERCISE 90 **SYNTHESIS OF SENTENCES**

Combine each pair of sentences by using the correlative conjunction "either...or" or "neither...nor."

1   One can go there by bus. One can also walk there.

_____

_____

2   Such a book is not interesting. It is not useful, either.

_____

_____

3   Your cash card may be in the drawer. It may be in your pocket.

_____

_____

4   The couple's garden is not big. It is not well-maintained, either.

_____

_____

POINTS / 5

EXERCISE 91   *SYNTHESIS OF SENTENCES*

- We can join sentences using nouns or noun phrases in apposition. Mark off these phrases with commas. [Example: My neighbor called on me. He is Mike. My neighbor, <u>Mike</u>, called on me.]
- We can join sentences using adverbs of manner. [Example: Ann protested. She repeated her protest many times. Ann <u>repeatedly</u> protested.]
- We can use participles or participle phrases to join sentences. [Example: He looked at the sky. He saw a hawk. <u>Looking at the sky</u>, he saw a hawk.]
- We can join sentences using prepositional phrases. [Example: He reached home. He received a shock. <u>On reaching home</u>, he received a shock.]
- We can join sentences using infinitives. [Example: She went closer. She wanted to see more clearly. She went closer <u>to see</u> more clearly.]
- We can join sentences using subordinate clauses. [Example: Peter did not go out. He was unwell. <u>As Peter was unwell</u>, he did not go out.]

Combine each pair of sentences into a longer simple sentence in any way you can.

1 The man sat down quietly. He thought things over.

_____

_____

2 The boy was taken aback. He jumped up uncontrollably.

_____

_____

3 At the bottom of the bridge lay a damaged car. It was swept away by a flood.

_____

_____

4 Here is something interesting. Would you like to see?

_____

_____

5 Do you know my boss? He is Mr. Washington.

_____

_____

POINTS   / 5

EXERCISE 92   *SYNTHESIS OF SENTENCES*

Combine each pair of sentences into a longer simple sentence in any way you can.

1 Noel's father helped me. He is a friendly person.

_____

_____

2 They reached their destination. It was early in the morning.

_____

_____

3 She received the air ticket. She made preparations for the trip.

_____

_____

4 The harbor was blocked by a big boat. It was damaged by tidal waves.

_____

_____

5 Roland jumped to his feet. He dashed after the petty thief.

_____

_____

EXERCISE 93

SYNTHESIS OF SENTENCES

Combine each pair of sentences into a complex sentence (main clause + subordinate clause).

1 Diana is wearing a large hat. It is decorated with pretty feathers.

_____

_____

2 Our teacher might not see us. That was our only hope.

_____

_____

3 Who dirtied the floor? Do you know?

_____

_____

4 How did you manage to dismiss your secretary? Tell me.

_____

_____

5 There was much to be done. We did not finish until midnight.

_____

_____

EXERCISE 94   SYNTHESIS OF SENTENCES

Combine each pair of sentences into a complex sentence (main clause + subordinate clause).

1 The men pushed hard. The truck would not move.

_____

_____

2 The fishing boat reached the pier. The people rushed on board immediately.

_____

_____

3 The police arrived at the scene of the crime. The criminal disappeared.

_____

_____

4 Peter ran to school. He did not want to be late.

_____

_____

5 You can have the book on one condition. You must keep it clean.

_____

_____

POINTS

/5

EXERCISE 95   *SYNTHESIS OF SENTENCES*

Combine each pair of sentences into a complex sentence (main clause + subordinate clause).

1 You cannot go. You have done your work.

_____

_____

2 All may go fishing. The weather is fine.

_____

_____

3 Our country is small. It is very prosperous.

_____

_____

4 You are wrong this time. I think so.

_____

_____

5 We don't like the new manager. He is very arrogant.

_____

_____

POINTS /5

EXERCISE 96 **THE PARALLEL STRUCTURE**

Parallel structure helps make sentences grammatically clear by using similar grammatical units to explain ideas in a sentence. Ideas can be expressed using gerunds, clauses, or other phrases. The ideas are joined using conjunctions. [Example: The question is to start working now or to go for further studies.]

In each of the following sentences, write the parallel sentence elements on the lines below.

1   Our population is made up of young people of different ages and old people of various cultural backgrounds.

_____

_____

2   Generally speaking, our people are courteous, conscientious and law-abiding.

_____

_____

3   Going to the movie theater and visiting big shopping centers are popular pastimes of our people.

_____

_____

4   The thief entered the room quietly, softly, and tactfully.

_____

_____

5   Some people like to trap others into innocent statements and then expose their errors in logic.

_____

_____

POINTS /5

EXERCISE 97   **THE PARALLEL STRUCTURE**

In each of the following sentences, write the parallel sentence elements on the lines below.

1   A religious leader warned the people that disasters lay ahead and that the world could be ruined.

_____

_____

2   Hawaii is both a center for international conferences and a paradise for tropical foods.

_____

_____

3   Betty accused not only her rival but also her rival's family.

_____

_____

4   They terrify residents, break windows, smash cars, and so on.

_____

_____

5   Anyone who wishes to write well must learn to think about points logically, organize ideas coherently, and express thoughts clearly.

_____

_____

POINTS /15

EXERCISE 98 TRANSITIONAL MARKERS/ CONNECTORS

A transitional marker is a word or phrase placed at or near the beginning of a sentence to indicate its relation to the preceding sentence. They can be used to show addition, cause and effect, comparison, contrast, concession, examples, summary and time relations. [Example: I agreed to accompany her to the library. <u>After all</u>, I wanted to borrow a book as well.]

Complete each sentence with a suitable transitional marker from the list. Use each marker <u>once</u>.

to illustrate	however	on the contrary	in other words	for example
as a result	in short	even though	besides	nevertheless
similarly	likewise	moreover	on the whole	then

1 This is not an economical way to get more water. _____, it is very expensive.

2 Everyone used less gas. _____, we were not short of energy.

3 Some countries have desalinisation projects. _____, no country can really afford to get water in this way.

4 Some people say Chinese is easy. Some others say it is difficult.

_____, opinions vary with regard to learning Chinese.

5 Many started to complain. Bill, _____, said that his work was not really appreciated.

6 _____ he tries hard, he can't get anywhere.

7 _____ doing the washing, Janet also went grocery shopping this morning.

8 Those girls like to play soccer. _____, those boys like to play football.

9 Jason works very long hours. _____, he spends a lot of time writing.

10 Some students study well. _____, they know how to manage their time properly.

11 His essay is full of errors. _____, it is wrong to use 'he' to replace 'Susan'.

12 Don't write in pencil. _____, write with a pen.

13 You must bring food along. _____, you need clothing.

14 Please learn English properly. _____, you can communicate more effectively.

15 I have marked all the examination booklets. _____, they are quite good.

POINTS /5

EXERCISE 99 **REDUCE ADJECTIVE CLAUSES TO PHRASES**

- An adjective clause with the verb in the passive voice can be shortened to a past participle phrase. [Example: Jason used to teach a course that was called Elements of Good Writing. Jason used to teach a course called Elements of Good Writing.]
- Adjective clauses with verbs in the active voice can sometimes be shortened to phrases using present participles. [Example: Christianity, which began in the west, later spread to other countries throughout the world. Christianity, beginning in the west, later spread to other countries throughout the world.]
- Adjective clauses can also be shortened by removing the relative pronoun and "be." [Example: At a seminar, I met Dr. Hugh, who is a professor of linguistics. At a seminar, I met Dr. Hugh, a professor of linguistics. / At a seminar, I met a professor of linguistics, Dr. Hugh.]

In each of the sentences below, change the adjective clause to the appositive phrase.

1 The book is based on a true story about Janet Lee, who was the founder of this orphanage.

_____

_____

2 The whole act, which is the length of four pages, is expected to be memorized by the students.

_____

_____

3 The first chapter, which is about the author's childhood, is the most touching.

_____

_____

4 The members of this club, who are approximately 2000 in number, participate in charity shows every year.

_____

_____

5 I know David, who is the director of this multi-national company.

_____

_____

NAME: .... DATE: ....

CLASS: ....

POINTS /5

EXERCISE 100

REDUCE ADJECTIVE CLAUSES TO PHRASES

In each of the sentences below, change the adjective clause to the adjective phrase with a past participle phrase.

1 The students follow a set of rules in school that is called 'The Official School Rules'.

_____

_____

2 The grooming classes, which are conducted each day, are very popular among the pet owners.

_____

_____

3 These who are achieving excellent grades will be rewarded.

_____

_____

4 A substance which is made up of atoms of different kinds is called a compound.

_____

_____

5 Jason's latest book, which is known as GEMS, is quite popular with English language learners.

_____

_____

EXERCISE 101

REDUCE ADJECTIVE CLAUSES TO PHRASES

In each of the sentences below, change the adjective clause to the adjective phrase with a present participle phrase.

1   The force which holds the solar system together is called gravitation.

_____

_____

2   Over 600 people, who represent different races and continents, attended this convention.

_____

_____

3   A person who travels in a foreign country will find the customs and traditions fascinating.

_____

_____

4   All the rooms have the same design, which consists of a balcony and a private bathroom.

_____

_____

5   The villagers contributed to numerous art fairs, which included weaving, painting and wood carving.

_____

_____

EXERCISE 102 *PHRASAL VERBS*

A phrasal verb is made up of a verb and a preposition or an adverb participle. [Example:
I <u>left out</u> a word. I <u>ran into</u> an old friend.]

Fill in each blank with a phrasal verb from the list. Be sure to use the correct verb
form, as shown in the examples above. Use each phrasal verb <u>once</u>.

turn out	back up	count in	count out	ferret out
stamp out	pick up	put off	take over	tide over
bear out	beef up	blow up	bottle up	break off
bring about	call off	draw up	let down	shake off

1 That factory often _____ high-precision instruments.

2 The tour is too expensive, please _____ me _____.
I can't afford it.

3 It is not difficult to _____ a new language if you really consider it
useful.

4 I will lend you some money to _____ you _____during
this period of difficulty.

5 Some small events have been _____ in the press.

6 Nancy's recklessness has _____ her ultimate failure.

7 You must try your best to help David. Don't _____ him

_____.

8 I often _____ my friends when they do something good.

9 Officials say that they will _____ abuses in the welfare program.

10 Because of the bad weather, the soccer match was _____.

11 Who can _____ you _____ if you accuse him of swindling?

12 Tell us how you feel. Don't _____ your feelings _____!

13 No one can _____ a pre-arranged meeting at will.

14 We will go fishing this afternoon. Shall we _____ you _____?

15 The government should do everything to _____ social ills.

16 Who will _____ the family business at the death of the father?

17 Some countries keep on _____ their military power.

18 Make sure that the agreement you have _____ is clear and accurate.

19 The old man found it hard to _____ some ailments.

20 The two neighbors quarreled and then _____ their relationship.

EXERCISE 103 *PHRASAL VERBS*

When we answer questions, we can replace the noun in the question with a pronoun. [Example: Did they call off the match? Yes, they called it off.]

Answer each of the questions affirmatively, using the phrasal verb in the parentheses. Replace the noun object with the pronoun object. Be sure to use the correct verb form. Follow the example above.

1 Did you test the new car? (try out)

_____

_____

2 Did you review your lessons before the examination? (go over)

_____

_____

3 Have you solved the problem? (figure out)

_____

_____

4 Will you clean the table, please? (wipe off)

_____

_____

5 Did the prisoner escape? (run away)

_____

_____

6 Can you complete the application forms? (fill out)

_____

_____

POINTS /8

EXERCISE 104 — *PHRASAL VERBS*

Answer each of the questions affirmatively, using the phrasal verb in the parentheses. Replace the noun object with the pronoun object. Be sure to use the correct verb form.

1 Have they considered the matter? (think over)

_____

_____

2 Has your grandmother recovered from her illness? (get over)

_____

_____

3 Are you going to rewrite the letter? (do over)

_____

_____

4 Did they finish all the food? (use up)

_____

_____

5 Do you telephone your girlfriend every day? (call up)

_____

_____

6 Would you please shut off the lights now? (turn off)

_____

_____

7 You can search for the information in the dictionary, can't you? (look up)

_____

_____

8 Was her application rejected? (turn down)

_____

_____

POINTS

10

EXERCISE 105 *PHRASAL VERBS*

In each of the following sentences, there is a phrasal verb. Write it down.

1 The man gave up his attempts to find a better job.

_____

2 The soldiers blew up the unexploded bomb.

_____

3 Don't leave out periods at the end of sentences.

_____

4 What did you do when you came across a difficult word?

_____

5 Because of the busy work schedule, we had to put off our trip overseas.

_____

6 Go on with your work while I am correcting your exercises.

_____

7 A burglar broke into Mr. Brown's house while he was out.

_____

8 The peace talks between the two neighboring countries have broken down for the third time.

_____

9 Everyone must stand up for his principles.

_____

10 More and more outdated shops are closing down.

_____

APPENDIX

Additional Notes

1 ACTIVE AND PASSIVE VOICE

If the subject of a sentence does something, the verb is in the active voice. If something is done to the subject, the verb is in the passive voice.

In the following two examples, verbs in (1a) and (2a) are in the active voice, while verbs in (1b) and (2b) are in the passive voice:

Examples:
1 (a) Peter bought a new dictionary.
   (b) A new dictionary was bought by Peter.
2 (a) Your boss will invite you to dinner.
   (b) You will be invited to dinner by your boss.

Note that only the transitive verb can be put into the passive voice, as only the transitive verb has an object.

The active voice can be changed into the passive voice according to the following steps:

1. Move the object of the active sentence to be the subject of the passive sentence.
2. Add the correct form of the verb 'be' according to the tense of the verb and the number of the subject.
3. Place the past participle of the verb after the verb 'be'. If there is a modal verb, it must be kept in this form:
   'modal verb + be + past participle'.
4. Move the subject of the active sentence to the back of the passive sentence with the aid of the preposition 'by'. If the subject of the active sentence is not important, omit it.
5. If there are two objects, use one of them (direct or indirect) to be the subject of the passive sentence; normally, the indirect object (that is, the person) is used.

   Examples:
   1 We must do the work. / The work must be done by us.
   2 All students will take the same examination. / The same examination will be taken by all students.
   3 Tom asked me a few questions. / I was asked a few questions by Tom.

4 Someone beat the sleeping cat. / The sleeping cat was beaten.
5 The police have arrested two thieves. / Two thieves have been arrested.

2 SENTENCE FORMATION

A sentence is made up of two parts: the **subject** and the **predicate**. These two parts combine to make a complete sentence. What are the subject and the predicate?

In a normal sentence, the subject appears at the beginning of the sentence, while the predicate comes after it.

The subject consists of one item or several items. The predicate also consists of one item or several items, as in the following chart:

Subject	Predicate
1 Birds	sing
2 The sun	shines.
3 Rumors	spread fast.
4 The manager of the building	checked every visitor with great care.

The subject is often a noun or noun-equivalent.

In (1) to (3), the subjects 'birds, the sun, rumors' are all nouns.

In (4), the subject 'the manager' is a noun with an adjective phrase 'of the building'.

As for the predicate, it may have one item or more. If it has only one item, that item must be the verb.

The simplest sentence is therefore a sentence with 'one subject + one verb'.

When the predicate consists of several items, the main item must be the verb; other items may be the object if the verb is transitive, an adverb / adverb equivalent, or both the object and the adverb / adverb equivalent.

In (1), the predicate is the verb 'sing'.

In (2), the predicate is the verb 'shines'.

In (3), the predicate is the verb 'spread' and the adverb 'fast'.

In (4), the predicate is the verb 'checked' and the object 'every visitor' and the adverb phrase 'with great care'.

The verb may be a linking verb. If so, it requires a complement, which may be one of the following:

1. An adjective / adjective phrase, e.g., The sky becomes dark. / Our economy is in good condition.
2. A noun, e.g., Helen is a singer.
3. A pronoun, e.g., The traitor is you.
4. A present participle, e.g., This morning's lesson was boring.
5. A past participle, e.g., Irene seems worried.
6. An adverb of place, e.g., The guest is here.
7. An adverb phrase of place, e.g., Who is in the kitchen?

The above complements are subjective since they say something more about each subject. Complements, however, can be objective when they refer to objects and make the meaning of each object complete.

Examples:

1 His parents named her Lucy.
2 The judge found him guilty.
3 William kept us waiting.
4 I believe him to be honest.
5 I find this book of great value.

In (1), the objective complement is a noun 'Lucy' referring to the object 'her'.

In (2) it is an adjective 'guilty' referring to the object 'him'.

In (3), it is a present participle 'waiting' referring to the object 'us'.

In (4), it is an infinitive 'to be honest' referring to the object 'him'.

In (5), it is an adjective phrase 'of great value' referring to the object 'book'.

3 TYPES OF SENTENCES (Part 1)

On the basis of **functions**, sentences can be divided into four types; that is, declarative, interrogative, imperative, exclamatory.

A ▬ DECLARATIVE SENTENCES

A **declarative sentence** or statement states a fact. For a positive statement, the sentence is affirmative. For a negative statement, the sentence is negative, indicated by the word, "not", "no", "none", "never", etc.

In the following sentences, 1a, 2a, 3a, 4a, 5a are affirmative sentences, while 1b, 2b, 3b, 4b, 5b are negative sentences.

Examples:

1 (a) Tom lives far from the school.
  (b) Tom does not live far from my house.

2 (a) All of us go to school early.
  (b) None of us go to school late.

3 (a) I have seen your uncle once.
  (b) I have never seen your aunt before.

4 (a) Tom's father is a businessman.
  (b) Tom's father isn't a teacher.

5 (a) They are now in London.
  (b) They are not in America.

B ▬ INTERROGATIVE SENTENCES

An **interrogative sentence** is used to ask a question, so an interrogative sentence is also called a question.

1. Most of the questions are general questions, which take 'Yes' or 'No' as answers. Hence, general questions are also called 'yes-no questions'.

Examples:

1 Are you a student? Yes, I am.
2 Does Andy know English? No, he doesn't.

2. The second type of question is alternative questions in which two answers are provided for your choice through the use of the conjunction 'or'.

Examples:

1 Is June a cook or a maid? She is a cook.
2 Will you stay for a night, or must you leave now? I shall stay for a night.

The second part of the question may be elliptical.

Examples:

1. Did they go to Hong Kong or (did they go to)London?
2. Will they come by car or (will they come) by bus?
3. Can you be there on Monday or (can you be there) on Tuesday?

3. The third type of question is asking about information known as '**informative questions**' formed with a question word, such as 'where, when, who, what, why, how' + auxiliary verb/modal verb + subject + principal verb.

   Examples:

   1. Where are you going?
   2. When will you come?
   3. What can you see?

4. The last type of commonly seen question is tag questions, formed by 'a statement + a question tag' with a comma in between.

   If the statement is affirmative, the question tag is negative, and vice versa.

   Also, the pronoun and the auxiliary/modal verb in the tag must be the same as they are in the statement. Finally, the tense in the tag must also agree with that in the statement.

   Examples:

   1. Helen is sad, isn't she?
   2. The pupils will come, won't they?
   3. She isn't happy, is she?
   4. They won't go, will they?

   The answer of 'Yes' or 'No' to a tag question is based on the nature of the statement. If the statement is positive, the answer is positive; if the statement is negative, the answer is negative.

   Hence the answers to the above examples are as follows:

   1. Yes, she is.
   2. Yes, they will.
   3. No, she isn't.
   4. No, they won't.

C ▬▶ IMPERATIVE SENTENCES

An **imperative sentence** is used to make a request or give an order.

1. The verb of an imperative sentence is in the present tense, and the subject is the second person 'you', which is often omitted.

   Examples:

   1. Stand there!
   2. Take a seat, please.
   3. Please shut the door.

2. To express the indirect order for the first or third person, we have to begin the imperative sentence with 'let'.

   Examples:

   1. Let me do it.
   2. Let him tell us.
   3. Let the boy come in.

D ▬▶ EXCLAMATORY SENTENCES

An **exclamatory sentence** is used to express emotional feelings like surprise, joy, anger, etc.

An exclamatory sentence is often introduced by '**what**' + noun or '**how**' + adjective / adverb.

Examples:

1. What a beautiful girl Susan is!
2. What a nice man you are!
3. How happy you look!
4. How sweetly Irene sings!

Note the difference between an exclamatory sentence and an interrogative sentence in word order:

	Exclamatory Sentence	Interrogative Sentence
1	How smart he is!	How smart is he?
2	How far you have run!	How far have you run?
3	What a good prize Sam gets!	What prize does Sam get?

4 TYPES OF PHRASES

A phrase is a group of words with some sense. It has no subject in itself but can be part of a sentence. The following are some phrases we often see.

1. **Noun phrase**
   A **noun phrase** does the work of a noun.
   Examples:
   1 The state of New Mexico lies in the southern part of the United States.
   2 When did you visit the capital of America?

2. **Adjective phrase**
   An **adjective phrase** does the work of an adjective. It is often formed with a 'preposition + noun'.
   Examples:
   1 Jason wrote a number of books on language learning.
   2 The people of different races live together harmoniously.

3. **Adverb phrase**
   An **adverb phrase** does the work of an adverb. Like adjective phrases, an adverb phrase is also often formed with a 'preposition + noun'.
   Examples:
   1 The boy ran across the road.
   2 Mary is standing near the door.

4. **Present participle phrase**
   Like an adjective phrase, a **present participle phrase**, introduced by a present participle, is a noun-modifying phrase.
   Examples:
   1 Hearing the noise, the boy jumped up.
   2 This is the road leading to the main library.

5. **Past participle phrase**
   Introduced by a past participle, a **past participle phrase** is also a noun-modifying phrase.
   Examples:
   1 Greatly shocked, the girl burst out crying.
   2 That is a socialist country led by the working class.

5 DIRECT AND INDIRECT OBJECTS

A number of verbs in English like 'give, bring, write, send, teach, buy, ask, etc.' take two objects in a sentence, direct and indirect.

1. **Direct objects**
   The **direct object** is usually about something, and the indirect object is about someone.
   Examples:
   1 I gave Anne a book.
   2 He bought the child a doll.

   In examples (1) and (2) above, 'Anne' and 'the child' are two persons and are two indirect objects; 'a book' and 'a doll' are two things and are two direct objects. The indirect object comes before the direct object.

2. **Indirect objects**
   The **indirect object**, however, can be moved to the back of the sentence with the aid of the preposition 'to' or 'for'.
   Examples:
   1 (a) I gave Anne a book.
     (b) I gave a book to Anne.
   2 (a) He bought the child a doll.
     (b) He bought a doll for the child.

6 DIRECT AND INDIRECT SPEECH

In **direct speech**, the speaker's exact words are enclosed in inverted commas, also known as quotation marks.

In **indirect speech** (or reported speech), the speaker's words are based on the direct speech with certain structural changes, including these:

1. The conjunction 'that' is used to introduce the indirect speech. If the tense of the reporting verb is in the past, all the present tense forms must be changed to the past, too.

Examples:

1 John said, "I am very well." / John said <u>that</u> he <u>was</u> very well.

2 She <u>said</u>, "I have done the work." / She said <u>that</u> she <u>had</u> done the work.

2. The pronoun and the possessive determiner are normally changed from the first person or second person to the third person.

   Examples:

   1 Jim said, "I like it." / Jim said that <u>he</u> liked it.

   2 Helen said, "I have done my work." / Helen said that <u>she</u> had done <u>her</u> work.

3. Determiners 'this, these' become 'that, those', and adverbs or adverb phrases of time have to change like these: (a) now to then; (b) today to that day; (c) yesterday to the day before; (d) tomorrow to the next day; (e) next week / next year, etc. to the following week / year, etc; (f) last night / week, etc. to the previous night / week, etc.

   Besides these, the adverb of place 'here' has to become 'there'.

   Examples:

   1 John said, "I am glad to be here this morning." / John said that he was glad to be <u>there that</u> morning.

   2 The teacher said, "I want to mark these scripts now." / The teacher said that she wanted to mark <u>those</u> scripts <u>then</u>.

Direct speech may be a declarative sentence, an interrogative sentence, an imperative sentence, or even an exclamatory sentence. The six examples above are all declarative sentences.

An indirect question, is introduced by the verb 'asked'. If the direct question starts with a question word like 'who, what, how, where, when, etc.', the same question word should be transferred to the indirect question.

Examples:

1 John said to me, "What are you doing?" / John asked me <u>what</u> I was doing.

2 "Where do you live?" the man asked Helen. / The man asked Helen <u>where</u> she lived.

If the question is not introduced by a question word, the reporting verb is then followed by the conjunction 'whether / if'.

Examples:

1 He said, "Will you go, Betty?" / He asked Betty <u>whether</u> she would go.

2 "Can you open the door for me?" she asked the boy. / She asked the boy <u>if</u> he could open the door for her.

In reporting a command or request, the indirect speech is introduced by the verb 'order' or 'request', followed by the object and the to-infinitive.

Examples:

1 Bill said to the girl, "Stop talking!" / Bill ordered the girl to stop talking.

2 He said to her, "Please help me." / He requested her to help him.

To simplify matters, we can use 'told' for both commands and requests.

Examples:

1 The teacher said to the boy, "Go out!" / The teacher told the boy to go out.

2 She said to Tom, "Please wait here." / She told Tom to wait there.

7 THERE IS / THERE ARE

'There' is an introductory subject.

1. **'There is + singular subject'**

   Example:

   There is a book on the table.

2. **'There are + plural subject'**

   Example:

   There are people in the room.

As a habit, **'any'** goes with **'questions'** or **'negative statements'**, while **'some'** goes with **'positive statements'**.

Examples:

1 Are there any books on the shelf?
Yes, there are some books on the shelf. /
No, there aren't any books on the shelf.

2 Was there any food left from the dinner last night?
Yes, there was some food left from the dinner last night. / No, there wasn't any food left from the dinner last night.

8 THE SUBJECT-VERB CONCORD

In English, if the **verb** in the predicate is in the present tense, it **agrees with the subject in person and number**.

The following are some important rules of the agreement between the verb and the subject.

1. Two or more singular subjects joined by the conjunction 'and' usually take a verb in the plural.

   Examples:
   1 John and his wife have just arrived.
   2 You, he and I are good friends.

2. When the subject is made up of two inseparable elements to express a unit or singular idea, the verb is in the singular.

   Example:
   Bread and butter is most people's breakfast.

3. Two singular subjects joined by either... or, neither...nor, or, nor take a verb in the singular number.

   Examples:
   1 Either the maid or the servant has broken the pot.
   2 Neither John nor Jill knows the answer to the problem.

   If one of the subjects is plural, the verb agrees with the subject nearest to it.

   Examples:
   1 Either the book or the magazines are on sale.

2 Neither the dogs nor the cat has been vaccinated.

4. When the subject is a collective noun, it takes a singular verb if the individuals in the noun is thought of as a whole.

   Example:
   The committee has accepted the proposal.

   If the individuals are considered separate, then the noun / pronoun is plural, and the verb is plural, too.

   Example:
   The jury were divided in their views, so they will meet again next week.

5. Indefinite pronouns, such as someone, everybody, something, nothing, etc. are singular in number and should be used with verbs in a singular sense.

   Examples:
   1 Somebody has forgotten to switch off the lights.
   2 Nothing is left undone.

6. Any noun after as well as, together with, etc. does not affect the actual number of the subject before it.

   Example:
   The manager as well as his secretary has been in the office for some time.

9 PRONOUN REFERENCE

The **pronoun** replaces the noun in a sentence. The pronoun agrees in person, number, gender and case with the noun referred to in the earlier context.

Examples:
1 The man plucked out a grey hair from his head.
2 We need money, but we often run out of it.
3 A person must restrict himself to doing what is right and useful.
4 Susan said that she did not like the man.

Pronouns like anyone, no one, nobody, each, everyone, somebody, someone, nothing, anything, everything, either, neither, etc. take a singular verb.

Examples:
1   Each was annoyed by the noise outside.
2   Nobody here has objected to such a plan.
3   Nothing is difficult, if properly done.

Pronouns like many, both, several, few, etc. take a plural verb.

Examples:
1   Many were absent yesterday.
2   Both of you are welcomed.
3   Several have not turned up yet.

Pronouns like some, any, none, all, etc. take either a singular or a plural verb, depending on the actual context.

Examples:
1   None of the information was accurate.
2   Some have agreed to come.
3   The news is old. All has to be discarded.
4   Here are the athletes. None of them have stopped practicing.
5   All the students were made to do some gardening.
6   I don't like the office equipment. Some is old-fashioned.

As a pronoun is a word of reference to its antecedent, it must be properly placed in a sentence, so that there is no doubt over the noun to which it refers.

10 SEQUENCE OF TENSES (II)

Generally speaking, the verb tense in the subordinate clause should agree with the verb tense in the main clause.

1.   When the verb in the main clause is in the past tense, the verb in the noun clause or adverb clause should also be in one of the past forms.

Examples:
1   He said that he was absent yesterday.
2   She failed because she did not work hard.

There are two exceptions to this rule:
(a)   When the noun clause expresses a truth or universal fact, the tense remains in the present tense.

Examples:
1   Who discovered that the earth goes round the sun?
2   The teacher said that honesty is the best policy.

(b)   In an adverb clause of comparison, any appropriate tense will do.

Examples:
1   Sam liked you better than he likes me.
2   She valued his friendship more than she values mine.

2.   When the verb in the main clause is in the present tense, the verb in the noun clause or adverb clause may be in the present tense or in any other suitable tense.

Examples:
1   Mary believes that she will pass the driving test.
2   The manager has just told us that he was ill yesterday.
3   He is lazy though he is intelligent.

3.   When the verb tense is in an adjective clause, it is somewhat free from the influence of the verb tense in the main clause.

Example:
James suggested the idea which was ignored, but which they are now criticizing, and they will eventually accept.

11 FUNCTIONS OF INFINITIVES

The infinitive retains some features of the verb, but it may be used as a verbal noun to function as a subject, object or complement. It has 'to' as the marker.

Examples:
1 To learn a foreign language takes time. (Infinitive phrase as the subject.)
2 I want to help him. (Infinitive phrase as the object of the verb.)
3 A student's main duty is to study. (Infinitive as the complement of verb 'be'.)

The infinitive can also be seen in some common verb patterns, including the one without 'to'.

Examples:
1 I saw a man jump into the river.
2 She said she heard the baby cry.
3 The master made the servant work very hard.
4 Nobody can let you go now.

12 FUNCTIONS OF GERUNDS

A **gerund** is marked by '-ing'. It functions as a verbal noun but retains some features of a verb.

It may be used as

1. **The subject**
   Example:
   Reading is a good hobby.

2. **The object of a transitive verb**
   Example:
   I don't remember having said it.

3. **The object of a preposition**
   Example:
   Jason was interested in doing the work assigned.

4. **The complement of a linking verb**
   Example:
   Sam's pastime is taking photos.

Besides these, there is an important verb pattern of the gerund when the verb is 'stop, enjoy, go, mind, etc.'

Examples:
1 Stop talking!
2 They enjoyed reading novels.

3 Some women go shopping every weekend.
4 Do you mind staying a little longer?

As both the infinitive and the gerund can become the subject of the sentence, they are often interchangeable.

Examples:
1 To play with sharp tools is dangerous. / Playing with sharp tools is dangerous.
2 To see is to believe. / Seeing is believing.

This is also true of the complement of the linking verb.

Example:
The main purpose is to train the learner to read effectively. / The main purpose is training the learner to read effectively.

However, when the gerund or the infinitive is used as the object of the verb, we should note the following three points:

1. Some verbs are followed by the infinitive only.
   Examples:
   1 I don't expect to find him here.
   2 Andy failed to get the job.
   3 Jenny refused to come.

2. Some verbs are followed by the gerund only.
   Examples:
   1 The boy admitted being careless.
   2 Judy denied having anything to do with him.
   3 She avoided seeing Tom.

3. Some verbs may be followed by the infinitive or the gerund.
   Examples:
   1 You must try to help him. / You must try helping him.
   2 When will you begin to do it? / When will you begin doing it?

13 LESS OFTEN USED 'CONTINUOUS TENSES'

In English, present and past continuous tenses are quite often used. However, there are three less-often-used continuous tenses: present perfect continuous, past perfect continuous, future perfect continuous.

1. **Present perfect continuous tense**

    The present perfect continuous tense is formed by the auxiliary verb 'have/ has' + been + present participle.

    Examples:
    1   I have been writing.
    2   You have been writing.
    3   He has been writing.

    The **negative** is formed with 'not' after 'have / has'.

    Examples:
    1   I have not been writing.
    2   You have not been writing.
    3   He has not been writing.

    The **interrogative** form is to move the auxiliary verb 'have / has' to the front of the subject.

    The **present perfect continuous tense** is used for an action which started in the past and is still continuing.

    Examples:
    1   I have been waiting for a long time, and he still hasn't turned up.
    2   He has been teaching in this school since 1980.

2. **Past perfect continuous tense**

    The past perfect continuous tense is formed with 'had + been + present participle'.

    Examples:
    1   I had been working.
    2   You had been working.
    3   He had been working.

    The **negative** is formed by adding 'not' after 'had'.

Examples:
1   I had not been working.
2   You had not been working.
3   He had not been working.

The **interrogative** form is to move the auxiliary verb 'had' to the front of the subject.

The **past perfect continuous tense** is to indicate a past action which started and continued before the other past action began.

Example:
We were told that some lazy workers had not been working for many days.

3. **Future perfect continuous tense**

    The future perfect continuous tense is formed by 'shall / will + have been + present participle'.

    Examples:
    1   I shall have been working here for exactly one month at the end of this week.
    2   You will have been working here for exactly one month at the end of this week.

The **negative** is formed with 'not' after 'shall / will'.

The **interrogative** form is to move the auxiliary verb 'shall / will' to the front of the subject.

The **future perfect continuous tense** is to indicate a future action which will start and continue in the future.

Example:
He will have been working for two hours before her arrival.

14 TYPES OF SENTENCES (Part 2)

According to construction, a sentence may be simple, compound, or complex.

We can divide a simple sentence into two parts: the subject, often a noun or pronoun, which usually comes before the predicate, which consists of the verb and the rest of the sentence.

Normally, the subject appears at the beginning of a sentence, while the predicate comes after it, as in the following chart:

Subject	Predicate
1 Birds	fly.
2 The sun	gives light.
3 Gossip	is often false.
4 The gate of a building	prevents people from entering.

A **simple sentence** belongs to one of the following subtypes:
declarative sentence, interrogative sentence, imperative sentence, exclamatory sentence.

1. A **declarative sentence** makes a statement or an assertion. It can be affirmative or negative.

   Examples:
   1 He lives in a big house. / He doesn't live in a small apartment.
   2 Jane is a teacher. / She isn't a student.
   3 All of us learn English. / None of us learn Latin.

2. An **interrogative sentence** asks a question.

   Examples:
   1 Are you a student?
   2 Will you go to the zoo?
   3 When can you do it for me?

3. An **imperative sentence** expresses a command or request.

   Examples:
   1 Come here!
   2 Open the door for me, please!

   In an imperative sentence, the subject 'you' is understood and is therefore left out. For the first or third person, 'let' is used.

   Examples:
   1 Let's go together this time.
   2 Let him come in.

4. An **exclamatory sentence** expresses a strong feeling like surprise, joy, anger, etc. It is normally formed with 'what + noun' or 'how + adjective/adverb'.

Examples:
1 What a beautiful dress it is!
2 What happiness the baby has brought them!
3 How pretty you look today!
4 How peaceful the countryside is!

15 TYPES OF SENTENCES (Part 3)

Now that we have dealt with the simple sentence, let us now discuss compound and complex sentences.

A ——■ Compound sentences

A **compound sentence** consists of two or more sentences joined by a coordinating conjunction 'and, or, but, so, for, etc.'. Such sentences are known as coordinate clauses because they are of the same rank and are equal in importance.

Examples:
1 Rain suddenly came, and we all got wet.
2 Control your passions, or they will control you.
3 Tom tried hard, but he still could not make it.
4 Tony ran fast, so he arrived first.
5 We will accept your proposal, for it looks good.

B ——■ Complex sentences

A **complex sentence** consists of a main or independent clause and one or more subordinate or dependent clauses joined by a subordinating conjunction.

According to the function in the sentence, a subordinate clause may do the job of a noun, adjective, or adverb and is called a **noun clause** (examples 1 and 2), an **adjective clause** (examples 3 and 4), or an **adverb clause** (examples 5 and 6).

Examples:
1 James said that he could not come tonight.
2 Tony denied that he had criticized Tom.
3 The time which is lost is lost for ever.

4   Do you know the gentleman <u>who is talking to Lily?</u>
5   Do it <u>before you forget!</u>
6   She could not come <u>because she was busy.</u>

1. **noun clause**

A noun clause is often introduced by the subordinating conjunction 'that'. It can be the subject of a sentence, the object of a transitive verb in the main clause, the subjective complement of a linking verb in the main clause, the objective complement, the appositive clause to a noun in the main clause, etc.

Examples:
1   <u>That she is not injured</u> is fortunate. (subject of 'is')
2   Nancy insisted <u>that she was right.</u> (object of the transitive verb 'insisted')
3   The fact is <u>that most Harvard graduates are achievement-oriented.</u> (subjective complement of the linking verb 'is')
4   I am sure <u>that everything will be fine in the end.</u> (objective complement)
5   Your assumption <u>that all will be fine</u> is not valid. (in apposition to the noun 'assumption')

When the noun clause is the object or objective complement, the conjunction 'that' can be omitted.

Examples:
1   Nancy insisted <u>she was right.</u>
2   I am sure <u>everything will be fine in the end.</u>

All the noun clauses introduced by 'that' are statements or declarative sentences. However, they may be questions, and questions are of two types. One has a question word.

Example:
<u>Where</u> is he?

The other one has no question word.

Example:
<u>Can</u> you sing?

When the first type of question becomes a noun clause, it is introduced by the existing question word followed by the subject and the verb.

Example:
I want to know <u>where he is.</u>

When the second type of question is turned into a noun clause, it is introduced by the conjunction 'whether' or 'if', followed by the subject and the verb.

Examples:
1   I want to know <u>whether you can sing.</u>
2   Do you know <u>if Helen will join us?</u>
    [(i) Can you sing? (ii) Will Helen join us?]

Besides these, a noun clause can be the object of a preposition in the main clause. But this noun clause is not introduced by the conjunction 'that'.

Example:
We judge people by <u>what they do.</u>

2. **adjective clause**

An adjective clause is introduced by a relative pronoun: who, which, that, whose, etc. It can also be introduced by a relative adverb: why, when or where.

An adjective clause, also called a relative clause, functions as a noun modifier. The modified noun is known as the 'antecedent'.

There are two types of adjective clauses: **restrictive** (defining) or **non-restrictive** (non-defining).

(a)   The **restrictive adjective clause** is an integral part of the antecedent, as it makes the antecedent distinctive. There is no comma between it and the antecedent.

Examples:
1   Who discovered <u>that the earth goes</u> round the sun?

2 A doctor is a person who cures patients.
3 A library is a place where people read and study.

(b) The **non-restrictive adjective clause** adds information to the antecedent. This information is additional, not so important; even if it is left out, it will not affect the identity or the essential meaning of the antecedent. This adjective clause is marked off by commas.

Examples:
1 Jason's latest book, which came out last month, has been a great success.
2 Do you know how to get to the club, which has become more and more famous?

In an adjective clause, the relative pronoun '**who**' is used with human beings.

Example:
The man who has a long beard is my uncle.

The relative pronoun '**which**' refers to animals or things.

Examples:
1 Have you noticed the cat which is approaching you?
2 Here is the book which the teacher recommended.

The relative pronoun '**that**' may be used with human beings, animals or things.

Examples:
1 I don't like women that talk too much.
2 Where did you get the kitten that you are holding?
3 The generation gap is a problem that concerns us all.

The relative pronoun '**whose**' is used to show possession, applicable to human beings, animals and things.

Examples:
1 The headmaster spoke to those whose work was below standard.

2 Can you wash the kitten whose body is dirty?
3 Some are attracted to that furniture whose design is special.

Concerning relative adverbs, when the antecedent is 'time', we use '**when**', 'place', we use '**where**', and 'reason', we use '**why**'.

Examples:
1 Can you still remember the good old days when we played together?
2 I wish to visit my old university where I studied 30 years ago.
3 You must give me the reason why you are often late for work.

3. **Adverb Clause**
An **Adverb clause** is introduced by a subordinating conjunction which helps determine the type of the adverb clause.

(a) For the **adverb clause of time**, the conjunction is 'when, since, before, after or while'.

Examples:
1 He had done the work before his father came home.
2 Give me a call when you are free.

(b) For the **adverb clause of reason**, the conjunction is 'because, since, as or now that'.

Examples:
1 Tom did not come because he was ill.
2 As Singapore is a small country, it is necessary to control its population.

(c) For the **adverb clause of condition**, use the conjunction 'if' or 'unless'.

Examples:
1 If you don't understand, please ask again.
2 Unless you try, you won't know how good you are.

(d) For the **adverb clause of concession**, the subordinating conjunction 'although / though' is used.

Examples:

1. <u>Although he is rich</u>, he is not arrogant.
2. <u>Though I have been there before</u>, I may go there again.

(e) For the **adverb clause of place**, use 'where / wherever'; for the **adverb clause of purpose**, use 'so that / in order that'; for the **adverb clause of result**, use 'so...that'; for the **adverb clause of comparison**, use 'as...as' or 'than'; and for the **adverb clause of manner**, use 'as, as if'.

Examples:

1. Go <u>where you like</u>.
2. <u>Wherever you go</u>, I will go with you.
3. We eat <u>so that we may live</u>.
4. They work hard <u>in order that they will be rewarded</u>.
5. Tom ran so fast <u>that he got the first prize</u>.
6. Tony is as tall <u>as I am</u>.
7. Susan is cleverer <u>than Betty (is)</u>.
8. I did <u>as I was told</u>.
9. She kicked the can <u>as if it were a ball</u>.

Of all the adverb clauses, those about time, reason, condition and concession are the most widely used. The position of the four types of clauses is flexible. They can come after the main clause or before it. However, it is generally felt that it would be more forceful for the subordinate clause to be placed before the main clause, where possible.

Examples:

1. After he had finished his homework, he played.
2. As she was ill, she was absent.
3. If it rains, don't go out.
4. Though John is lazy, he is intelligent.

16 'IT' AS AN INTRODUCTORY SUBJECT TO REPRESENT TO-INFINITIVE / PHRASE

The pronoun **'it'** can be used **as an introductory subject**, while the logical subject is moved to the end of the sentence. In such a sentence, 'it' represents the logical subject 'to-infinitive / phrase'. It is often used under the following circumstances:

1. Shifting a long subject, the infinitive phrase, to the back of the sentence.

   Example:

   <u>It</u> is not unusual <u>for a woman to become a minister</u>.

2. Going with linking verbs seem, appear, feel, sound, etc.

   Examples:

   1. <u>It</u> seems a pity **to waste time**.
   2. <u>It</u> appears unlikely **for him to succeed**.
   3. <u>It</u> sounds reasonable **to accept his proposal**.

3. Going with verbs require, need, take, cost, delight, make, irritate, annoy, amuse, etc.

   Examples:

   1. <u>It</u> delighted me **to have come to know you**.
   2. <u>It</u> took the workers two hours **to clean the whole house**.
   3. <u>It</u> irritated him **to be asked to do the work all over again**.
   4. <u>It</u> made them nervous **to know about the company's problem**.
   5. <u>It</u> cost her fifty dollars **to see a dentist**.

17 'IT' AS AN INTRODUCTORY SUBJECT TO REPRESENT GERUND / GERUND PHRASES

'It' can be used to act **as an introductory subject** for a gerund or gerund phrase so as to enable the gerund or gerund phrase to be moved to the back of the sentence, just like we have done for the 'to-infinitive / phrase' in the previous topic.

'**It**' is always seen in 'It is no good, It is no use / useless, It is worthwhile, etc.'.

Example:

> It is no good <u>pretending to know what you don't know</u>.

'It' is also often used in constructions like 'It is fun, It is an awful job, It is hard, etc.'.

Example:

> It is fun <u>playing games with children</u>.

18 'IT' AS AN INTRODUCTORY OBJECT TO REPLACE AN INFINITIVE PHRASES OR GERUND PHRASES

'**It**' may serve as an **introductory object** for an infinitive phrase or gerund phrase. The phrase in this case should be shifted to the back of the sentence as an objective complement.

Examples:

1. We consider it our duty to defend our country.
2. He did not consider it worthwhile spending too much time on playing.

Have you written such bad sentences?

3. We consider to defend our country our duty.
4. He did not consider spending too much time on playing worthwhile.

If 'It' is not used, (1) becomes (3), and (2) becomes (4).

19 THE INVERTED ORDER

The normal word order of an English sentence is 'subject + predicate'. This kind of word order is called the natural order.

If the verb (usually an auxiliary verb) in the predicate and the subject are changed in position, the sentence is in the inverted order.

The inverted order or inversion is divided into the grammatical inversion and the emphatic inversion.

1. **Grammatical inversion**

   The grammatical inversion is obligatory. That means inversion is necessary. It includes these types of sentences:

   (a) Questions:

   > *Examples:*
   > 1. Can you come?
   > 2. Where do you live?

   (b) Imperative sentences indicating 'wishes':

   > *Examples:*
   > 1. May God bless you!
   > 2. Long live the Queen!

   (c) Expletive sentences with 'there':

   > *Examples:*
   > 1. There are many pupils in the playground.
   > 2. There goes your boss.

   (d) Sentences joined by 'neither / nor, so':

   > *Examples:*
   > 1. Sam has never been late; neither have I.
   > 2. Tom can run fast. So can Bob.

   (e) Some adverb clauses of condition with 'if' omitted:

   > *Examples:*
   > 1. Were I you, I would not say it.
   > 2. Had you tried again, you would have got it.

2. **Emphatic inversion**

   The emphatic inversion consists of the following three types:

   (a) Sentences with a negative adverb / adverb phrase at the beginning:

   > *Examples:*
   > 1. Never before have I seen such an awful movie.
   > 2. Under no circumstances can you bully him.

   (b) Sentences with 'not only, only by':

   > *Examples:*
   > 1. Not only does Micah know English, he also knows Chinese.

2   Only by doing it this way can you succeed.

(c)   Sentences with adverb particles:
Examples:
1   Up jumped the kitten.
2   In came the visitor.

20 ABSOLUTE CONSTRUCTION

An absolute construction is an independent participle phrase with a subject of its own.

Many absolute constructions are formed by using 'being' or 'having' after the subject.

Examples:
1   It being a fine day, we went swimming.
2   The car having been damaged, it was sent to the workshop.

21 ORDER OF ADJECTIVES IN A SENTENCE

When two or more adjectives appear in the same sentence, they must be arranged in a logical way.

In general, when a few adjectives of different types occur successively, they are arranged according to this order:

1.   At the beginning of the sentence: **determiners** like 'the, your, this'.

2.   Second position: **possessive case** like 'a man's, Mary's'.

3.   Third position: **ordinals** like 'first, next, last'.

4.   Fourth position: **numbers** like 'three, several, many'.

5.   Fifth position: **adjectives of quality** like 'clever, handsome'.

6.   Sixth position: **size, shape, length** like 'small, round, long'.

7.   Seventh position: **colors** like 'white, green, purple'.

8.   Eighth position: **nations** like 'English, American'.

9.   Ninth position: **attributive nouns** like 'flower vase, tea party'.

Examples:
1   Joelle has a white silk handkerchief.
2   Mr. Brown's first public speech was a great success.
3   The artist's first two expensive oil paintings can be seen in the museum.

Obviously, a series of adjectives can be orderly arranged to describe the same noun. The adjectives in each sentence above are different in nature. The adjectives of the same nature; that is, adjectives of quality, can also be arranged one after another.

Examples:
1   Tom seems to be a dull, tired, and sleepy man.
2   Yesterday was windy, stormy, and unpleasant.

As a rule, we have to read each of the adjectives in examples (1) and (2) above with some stress and a pause. In writing, a comma must be used to separate each of them. As for the order of arrangement, polysyllabic (longer) adjectives tend to come after monosyllabic ones, and adjectives with more important meanings appear after less important ones.

22 SYNTHESIS OF SENTENCES

Synthesis of sentences means joining two or more sentences together to make a longer one. This is a useful sentence construction exercise. It gives you practice in using a variety of different constructions. It helps you to avoid writing too many short sentences, which can become monotonous.

This, however, does not mean that a long sentence is better than a short one. On the contrary, you should avoid writing sentences that are unreasonably long and tedious. They often become difficult to follow and result in mistakes. Short sentences are often clearer and easier to understand.

However, too many short sentences soon become boring and the reader's interest is lost. That is why you should aim at variety in the length and construction of sentences.

Here are some commonly used ways to join sentences to achieve variety.

1. Using **conjunctions** 'and, or, but, so, for, etc.' to form compound sentences.

2. Using **nouns / noun phrases in apposition** marked off by commas.

   Example:
   My neighbor called on me. He is Mike.
   My neighbor, <u>Mike</u>, called on me.

3. Using **adverbs of manner**.

   Example:
   Anna protested. She repeated her protest many times.
   Anna <u>repeatedly</u> protested.

4. Using **participles / participial phrases**.

   Example:
   He looked at the sky. He saw a hawk.
   <u>Looking at the sky</u>, he saw a hawk.

5. Using **prepositional phrases**.

   Example:
   He reached home. He received a great shock.
   <u>On reaching home</u>, he received a great shock.

6. Using **infinitives**.

   Example:
   She went closer. She wanted to see more clearly.
   She went closer <u>to see</u> more clearly.

7. Using **a subordinate clause**.

   Example:
   Peter did not go out. He was unwell.
   <u>As Peter was unwell</u>, he did not go out.

23 THE PARALLEL STRUCTURE

A **parallel structure** is used to put parallel ideas in parallel grammatical units.

If one idea in a sentence is expressed by a phrase, other equal ideas should also be expressed by phrases.

If one idea is expressed by an infinitive, a gerund, or a clause, other equal ideas should also be expressed by duplicate grammatical constructions.

Parallel structure or parallelism helps make sentences grammatically clear by emphasizing their close relation in thought.

How to achieve parallelism, then?

1. **Link parallel sentence elements by a coordinating conjunction.**

   Examples:
   1. A good writer needs precision and originality.
      (Noun + Noun)
   2. The philosopher analyzed, discussed, questioned, and generalized. (4 verbs)
   3. The question is to start working now or to go for further studies. (2 infinitive phrases)

2. **Link parallel sentence elements by correlative conjunctions.**

   Examples:
   1. You can either take it or leave it.
   2. The woman can neither speak English nor write Chinese.

3. **Sentence elements must be parallel in meaning as well as in form.**

   Example:
   Being friendly and good-natured, Jose welcomed his guests hospitably. ('and' joins two adjectives with commendable meanings)

24 TRANSITIONAL MARKERS / CONNECTORS

A transitional marker is a word or phrase placed at or near the beginning of a sentence to indicate its relation to the preceding sentence. Different transitional markers are used for different purposes.

The following are some of the commonly seen ones:

1. **Addition**

   Examples:

   and, also, again, besides, furthermore, moreover, in addition, first, second, too, etc.

2. **Cause and effect**

   Examples:

   therefore, thus, accordingly, as a result, etc.

3. **Comparison**

   Examples:

   likewise, similarly, in like manner, etc.

4. **Contrast**

   Examples:

   however, still, in contrast, in spite of, on the contrary, on the other hand, etc.

5. **Concession**

   Examples:

   after all, even though, etc.

6. **Examples**

   Examples:

   for example, that is, to illustrate, in other words, etc.

7. **Summary**

   Examples:

   in brief, to sum up, in short, as a conclusion, etc.

8. **Time relations**

   Examples:

   afterwards, meanwhile, first, then, finally, after, before, later, etc.

25 REDUCTION: ADJECTIVE CLAUSES TO PHRASES

Adjective clauses (or relative clauses) can often be reduced to become **phrases** with the same functions.

First of all, an adjective clause with the verb in the passive voice may be shortened to be a past participle phrase functioning as an adjective phrase.

To form such a phrase, we have to eliminate the relative pronoun and the auxiliary verb 'be'.

Example:

Steph used to teach a course that was called Elements of Good Writing.
Steph used to teach a course called Elements of Good Writing.

Besides, some adjective clauses with verbs in the active voice may also be shortened to be adjective phrases in the form of present participles.

To form such a phrase, we have to omit the relative pronoun 'who, which, or that' and then turn the verb into the present participle.

Example:

Islam, which began in Arabia, spread quickly to many other countries throughout the world.
Islam, beginning in Arabia, spread quickly to many other countries throughout the world.

Finally, non-restrictive adjective clauses (that is, adjective clauses that use commas) can be shortened to be appositive phrases by removing the 'relative pronoun + be'.

Example:

At a seminar, I met Dr. Hugh, who is a professor of linguistics.
At a seminar, I met Dr. Hugh, a professor of linguistics. / At a seminar, I met a professor of linguistics, Dr. Hugh.

26 PHRASAL VERBS

A **phrasal verb** is made up of a verb and a preposition or an adverb participle.

Like a finite verb, a phrasal verb is a complete verb unit with a specific meaning and sometimes with more than one meaning.

A phrasal verb normally consists of two words like call up, look into, etc.

There are also three-word verbs like do away with, look back on, etc.

Phrasal verbs are of two types, **separable** and **inseparable**.

1. **Separable phrasal verbs**

    (a) For a separable phrasal verb, if the object is a noun, it can be placed after the phrasal verb or between the two parts of the phrasal verb.

         Example:
             I left out a word. / I left a word out.

         If the object is a pronoun, the phrasal verb must be separated.

         Example:
             I left it out.

    (b) The object of an inseparable phrasal verb, be it a noun or pronoun, must be placed after the phrasal verb.

         Example:
             I ran into an old friend. / I ran into him.

2. **Inseparable phrasal verbs**

    Three-word phrasal verbs are inseparable.

    Examples:
    1   I got out of the cab. / I got out of it.
    2   Can we do away with bad customs? / Can we do away with them?

NOTES

NOTES